AUTHOR'S NOTE (Nov. 1979)

The manuscript for this handbook was submitted for publication more than three years ago. Since that time there have been new research developments that should be noted. Also, some errors in terminology appearing in the book need correction. Following are specific corrections and additions:

Page 6 — Mr. Steve Cannings of Penticton is acknowledged for his photographic contributions to the book. I would also like to thank Mr. Peter L. Macnair and Mr. Alan L. Hoover of the Ethnology Division, and Dr. Robert D. Levine and Dr. Barbara Efrat of the Linguistics Division, British Columbia Provincial Museum, and Dr. Andrea Laforet of the National Museum of Man, Ottawa, for their supplementary criticisms and suggestions.

Page 22 — According to current linguistic evidence, there are considered to be two distinct Nootkan languages on Vancouver Island: Nootka proper (including Northern and Central dialects), from Cape Cook to Barkley Sound, and Nitinat, from Barkley Sound to Port Renfrew. The Makah on the Olympic Peninsula of Washington comprise a third language group. Niska and Gitksan are currently considered to be separate dialects of a single language known as Nass-Gitksan. There is also evidence for the existence of a third Tsimshian language, now extinct, known as Southern Tsimshian.

Page 23 — There is now some evidence that a very ancient relationship exists between Kootenay and the Salishan languages.

Pages 39 and 40 — Twined baskets were not decorated by the process of imbrication as implied; imbrication is a technique used only in decorating coiled baskets. False embroidery and overlay were techniques used to decorate twined baskets. Therefore, on page 40 delete "imbricating" and on page 39, and elsewhere throughout the text, bear this distinction in mind.

Page 45 — Instead of "halibut" read "black cod".

Page 79 — Instead of "cross-brace" read "thwart". The indication that "thwarts" were fixed with pegs is misleading; they were usually sewn into place.

Page 82 — Instead of "plaited", read "twisted" (occurs twice).

Page 103 — For the section starting, "Sometimes baskets and hats were ..." and ending "... natural mineral paints.", substitute the following: The Haida decorated their spruce-root baskets by false embroidery or by the substitution or dyed wefts for naturally coloured ones. The Tlingit decorated their baskets with false embroidery. Haida and Tlingit hats were generally decorated by painting designs on the finished products, using charcoal or natural mineral paints.

Page 113 – The section starting, "The Haida and St
and ending, "... of the fisherman's success." is mislea
The Coastal Indians often made curved fish-hooks frou
by the trunk ends of limbs of rotting, fallen hemlock
hooks were usually barbed with bone or iron. The Haid
also used by neighbouring groups for ground fishing,
example of one type of such a hook. According to the la
of Masset, the ends of the strongly curved black-cod h
apart with a small stick, which was released to the surfa
was caught as an indicator of the fisherman's success.

Page 173 – Instead of "black cod and octopus", read
possibly rock cod. Some Nootkan groups also used
octopus."

General – The work of Dr. Janet Friedman on wood identific
referred to in preparing the manuscript for this book. In ad
identifications of innumerable wooden objects and fragments
the Ozette Site in Washington, she has identified some of
artifacts in the collection of the Ethnology Division of
Columbia Provincial Museum and her results have been reveal
some cases, unexpected. Hopefully, in future, more of the plan
found in artifacts in museum collections will be positively
through microscopic examination.

Additional References:
Efrat, Barbara (Editor), 1978: "The Victoria Conference on North
    Languages". British Columbia Provincial Museum Heritage Reco
    4, Victoria.
Friedman, Janet, 1975: "The Prehistoric Uses of Wood at the O
    Archaeological Site". PhD. Dissertation, Department of Anthropol
    University of Washington, Seattle.
.........., 1978: "Wood Identification by Microscopic Examination". Brit
    Columbia Provincial Museum Heritage Record No. 5, Victoria.

N.J.7

BRITISH COLUMBIA PROVINCIAL MUSEUM

HANDBOOK No. 38

Plants In British Columbia Indian Technology

by
NANCY J. TURNER

Province of British Columbia
Ministry of Provincial Secretary
and Government Services
Provincial Secretary

Published by the British Columbia Provincial Museum,
Victoria

First edition - - - - - - - - 1979

Canadian Cataloguing in Publication Data.

Turner, Nancy J., 1947–
Plants in British Columbia Indian Technology.

(Handbook — British Columbia Provincial Museum;
no. 38 ISSN 0068-1628)

Bibliography: p. 287.
Includes index.
ISBN 0-7718-8117-7

1. Indians of North America—British Columbia—Industries.
2. Ethnobotany—British Columbia.
3. Botany, Economic—British Columbia.
I. Title. II. Series: British Columbia Provincial Museum.
Handbook—British Columbia Provincial Museum; no. 38.

E78.B9T87   581.6'4'09711   C79-092009-3

PREFACE

This is the third handbook of the British Columbia Provincial Museum dealing with the uses of plants by the native peoples of British Columbia. The previous handbooks covered the subject of Food Plants—the first on peoples of the Coast (Handbook No. 34), the second on Interior peoples (Handbook No. 36). In the present volume concerning plants in native technology I have combined the uses of plant materials by Coastal and Interior peoples, since there is considerable overlap between the Coast and Interior in the species of plants used for technological purposes.

As a child I used to watch with fascination the late Kwakiutl Chief Mungo Martin at Thunderbird Park in Victoria hewing massive animal forms from red cedar logs with nothing more than a small hand adze and a chisel. From that time on, my respect and appreciation for the knowledge and technological skills of native peoples has grown. Examining the delicate baskets with their intricate designs, the perfectly symmetrical canoes, the tools and fishing equipment, the kerfed boxes, the giant feast dishes, and any number of other items to be seen in museums and private collections, one is impressed with the workmanship and industry of the men and women who made them. A greater appreciation, however, comes not from admiring these items but from trying to make them oneself.

My first effort at imitating native technology was to make a small cat-tail mat, under the kind guidance and direction of the late Christopher S. Paul of the Tsartlip Reserve at Brentwood. By the time I had finished gathering and preparing the materials for this modest effort and constructing it according to traditional techniques, my admiration for native artisans had increased tenfold. Later, at Masset on the Queen Charlotte Islands, Mrs. Florence Davidson taught me how to make twined cedar-bark baskets, and guided me through the long and arduous procedures of collecting, splitting, and drying the bark, then weaving it in the proper way. My basket took many days to complete and looked like the work of a little child compared to her beautiful cedar-bark products, but I was quite proud of my efforts and once again my appreciation of native workmanship, both past and present, took a giant step upward.

Many are inclined to believe that native technological skills are a thing of the past. It is true that the number of items being made has decreased considerably within the last century, and that many of today's Indian craftsmen are of the oldest generation. Some skills, such as the making of dugout and birch-bark canoes by traditional methods and the old-time techniques of dyeing with natural mineral and vegetable dyes, have with few exceptions vanished completely. Nevertheless, young people in native communities are becoming increasingly aware of the rich cultural heritage of past generations, and the future of many technological arts looks bright indeed. By imitating the works of their forefathers, as seen now only in museums, modern native artists, particularly carvers, have been able to recapture and even improve upon the skills and techniques of the past. Dishes, spoons, masks, kerfed boxes, and beautifully imbricated baskets of spruce root, split cedar root, sedges, and other materials, are still made, and are sold to the public through gift shops, such as that of the British Columbia Provincial Museum, and privately by the artists themselves.

I have been privileged to have learned about plants used in native technologies from many knowledgeable and respected members of the native communities of the Province. They generously contributed their time and expertise to my studies, and I am forever indebted to them. I have already mentioned Christopher Paul and Florence Davidson. Others include: Mrs. William Matthews and her late husband of Masset; the late George Young, Miss Maude Moody, Miss Agnes Moody, Solomon Wilson and his late wife, Emma, and the late Mrs. Becky Pearson of Skidegate; Mrs. Peter Kelly of Vancouver; Mrs. Margaret Siwallace, the late David Moody, and Mrs. Felicity Walkus of Bella Coola; Mrs. Cecelia August of Sechelt; Andy Natrall, Sr., Louis Miranda, and the late Dominic Charlie of North Vancouver; the late Mr. and Mrs. Richard Harry of the East Saanich Reserve; the late Mrs. Lucy Brown and Mrs. Agnes Cranmer of Alert Bay; Bob Wilson and the late Mr. and Mrs. Tom Johnson of Fort Rupert; George Ignace, the late Mike Tom and his wife, "Mrs. Mike," and Mrs. Alice Paul and her son Larry Paul of Hesquiat; Luke Swan of Manhousat; Sam Mitchell of Fountain; the late Mrs. Martina LaRochelle of Lillooet;

4

Charlie Mack and Baptiste Ritchie of Mount Currie; Miss Annie York of Spuzzum; Louis Phillips of Lytton; Selina Timoyakin, Larry Pierre, Mr. and Mrs. Willie Armstrong, and Martin Louie of Penticton; Harry Robinson of Keremeos; Mrs. Eliza Archie of Canim Lake; Mrs. Aimee August of Chase; the late Frank White-head and Mrs. Mary Paul of St. Mary's Mission, Cranbrook; and Mrs. Catherine Grevelle of Tobacco Plains. Without these people this book could never have been written. I sincerely hope they and their families enjoy it and view it with a feeling of pride.

I would also like to thank Mr. R. Bouchard and Ms. D. I. D. Kennedy of the British Columbia Indian Language Project, Victoria, for permission to include information on plants used by the Mainland Comox people which they recorded from Mrs. Rose Mitchell, Bill Mitchell, the late John Mitchell, and Mrs. Jeannie Dominick, all of Squirrel Cove near Powell River, and for information on plants used by the Shuswap, which they recorded from Mrs. Aimee August and the late Isaac Willard of Chase. I am also grateful for the use of material from Kennedy and Bouchard's unpublished manuscripts on native fishing technologies as listed in the References. Kennedy has generously allowed me to use many of her photographs of Indian artifacts, which are published with the permission of the R. H. Lowie Museum of Anthropology at the University of California, Berkeley, the Smithsonian Institution in Washington, D.C., the Field Museum of Natural History in Chicago, Illinois, the American Museum of Natural History in New York, and the National Museum of Man in Ottawa. David Rozen of Victoria provided some information on the use of black hawthorn which he obtained from Abel Joe of the Cowichan Reserve. He also compiled ethnobotanical information from the unpublished notes of Jenness, cited in the References. David Ellis of the Queen Charlotte Islands, working with Luke Swan of Manhousat, also contributed information used in this handbook. Dr. Brent Galloway of The Coqualeetza Education and Training Centre, Sardis, B.C., kindly provided information on reed canary-grass, used for basketry by the Upper Stalo.

Many, many, others, including all of the linguists I have had the pleasure of working with over the last few years, have contributed to this book in no small way. I would also like to acknowledge the following: the late Freeman King of Victoria for inspiration and encouragement; Dr. Marcus A. B. Bell of the Biology Department, University of Victoria, and Dr. Roy L. Taylor, Director of the Botanical Garden, University of British Columbia, for their support and advice during my university years when much of my research was carried out; R. Yorke Edwards, Director of the British Columbia Provincial Museum, Dr. Adam F. Szczawinski, former Curator of Botany, now retired, and Dr. T. C. Brayshaw, Associate Curator of Botany at the British Columbia Provincial Museum for advice and financial support; Dr. R. T. Ogilvie, present Curator of Botany at the British Columbia Provincial Museum, for his critical reading of the manuscript; my student assistant for two summers, Ms. Kathleen Cowen, for her enthusiastic dedication, especially during field trips; Mr. Harold Hosford of the British Columbia Provincial Museum and Dr. Jack Maze of the Botany Department, University of British Columbia, for their editorial counsel; and my husband, Robert D. Turner, for his continuing moral support, and for contributing his photographic and drafting expertise to this project.

The Ethnology Division of the British Columbia Provincial Museum kindly allowed my husband to photograph a number of the artifacts in the Museum Collection and permitted us to include them in this book. The photographs taken in the early part of the century by E. S. Curtis are reproduced courtesy of the Provincial Archives of British Columbia. Photographs were also contributed by Mr. Tom Sowerby of Victoria and Mr. David Polster of Calgary.

TABLE OF CONTENTS

7

INTRODUCTION

The importance of plant foods and medicines to native peoples is well appreciated, but the role of plants in native material cultures, in many cases even more vital, is often overlooked. In British Columbia, where the winters are long and cold, where most foods must be cooked to make them palatable, where waterproof clothing and watertight shelters are indispensable, where the most efficient means of transportation in the early days was by water, where the native hunting/fishing/gathering economy required a myriad of special tools, and where metal of any type was relatively rare and pottery virtually unheard of, plant materials were not only useful but absolutely essential to survival.

Heat, shelter, transportation, clothing, implements, nets, ropes, and containers—necessities of life in the Pacific Northwest environment—were all afforded by the great abundance and variety of vegetation in the area. Additionally, plants were applied by native peoples in various non-essential but nevertheless important ways, such as for decoration and ornamentation, as scents, cleansing agents, and insect repellents, and in recreational activities.

Over the centuries, the native peoples of British Columbia have become highly skilled in the arts of working with plant materials. The cedar-wood canoes, totem poles, and kerfed boxes of the Coastal groups, especially those of the central and northern regions, are thought by many to be the most superb examples of woodworking craftsmanship to be found anywhere, and the coiled split cedar-root baskets of the Interior Salish peoples, with their intricate imbricated designs, are world famous. There are innumerable other equally impressive examples of proficiency in the utilization of plants and plant products.

It is the purpose of this handbook to provide information on the many different types of plants used as materials by British Columbia Indians, and at the same time to describe how these plants were employed and by which cultural and linquistic groups. Hopefully this book will be of interest to many different segments of the population—to Indian people seeking information about their past cultures, to professionals such as archaeologists, ethnol-

9

ogists, and botanists wishing to investigate certain aspects of material culture, to identify artifact materials, or to learn more about the practical applications of plants, and finally to members of the general public of both "armchair" and "do-it-yourself" varieties. All of these groups have been kept in mind during the planning and writing of the book. An effort has been made to be as complete and detailed as possible, at the same time keeping technical language to a minimum. Photographs are included of the plants themselves to aid in identification and of various artifacts made from plant materials to give the reader a better understanding of the practical aspects of plant utilization.

For the "do-it-yourself" enthusiasts who wish to employ some of the plants mentioned in this book for carving, weaving, or some other form of manufacture the possibilities are limitless. However, a note of caution must be interjected: almost any large-scale harvesting of plant materials—bark, roots, wood, or stems—is detrimental to the plants involved, and may affect their survival as individuals or local populations. With some plants, such as stinging nettle, Indian hemp, tule, or cat-tail—all herbaceous perennials—the gathering of stems or leaves is not likely to deplete the populations to any measurable degree, since these plants tend to grow in large patches and the rootstocks will grow new stems the following year. Many other species, especially trees, are not as abundant and do not regenerate as easily.

If the bark is removed around the entire circumference of a tree, the tree will be killed immediately. Even if the bark is only partially stripped off, it is still injurious to the tree, leaving the wood exposed to insect and fungal infestations and decreasing the plant's capacity to transport water and nutrients from the roots. Of course, harvesting wood is even more detrimental, because it usually involves cutting down the entire tree. Some species, such as western yew—particularly larger specimens—have become rare in certain localities, a situation due at least in part to over-zealous harvesting by wood carvers. The potential user of plant materials is urged to consider carefully the consequences of his harvesting activities and to practise the utmost care and discretion in removing any plants or parts of plants from any natural area.

FORMAT

Following the introductory discussions on the physical environment of British Columbia, the Indian peoples, and the general use of plants as materials by British Columbia Indians, is the listing of individual plant species with their botanical descriptions, habitats, distributions in the Province, and the ways in which they were employed in native technology. The order in which the plants are listed is partially botanical and partially practical. The major evolutionary groupings are maintained: Algae, Lichens, Fungi, Mosses, Ferns and Fern-allies, Conifers, and Flowering Plants. The Flowering Plants are further divided into two large subgroups, the Monocotyledons and Dicotyledons.

The Ferns, Conifers, and Flowering Plants are classed in family groups, which are presented in alphabetical order of the scientific family name. Within the major groups of the lower plants and the family groups of the higher plants, species are listed in alphabetical order of their scientific names. Common or colloquial names of both species and families are given at the left side of the page, while the corresponding scientific terminology is given on the right side. Alternate common names are included where appropriate. Local names which have limited application and which are not necessarily correct are given in quotation marks.

In some cases, such as with lichens, mosses, ferns, and grasses, a general discussion of the uses of an entire group of plants is provided, as well as a more detailed treatment of the species of greatest technological importance with the groups. Many plants played minor roles in British Columbia Indian technology, being used casually or by only one group. These were not considered significant enough to be included in the main portion of the text, but are listed at the end in an Appendix.

Vegetation and native cultures do not change at political borders. Thus, many of the plants discussed in this book were used in similar ways by the native peoples of neighbouring areas—the Tlingit of Alaska, the Makah, Quileute, and various Coast Salish groups of western Washington, the Okanagan and other Interior Salish groups of central and eastern Washington, the Flathead and

Kootenay of Montana, and the Blackfoot of Alberta, to name just a few. Information on the material uses of plants by these groups was included where available and when it contributed in any way to the discussions of British Columbia Indian plant technology.

Following the appendix are the Glossary, Reference List, and Index. The reference section includes literature consulted during the preparation of the book (*see* Sources of Information) as well as suggested reading material for those wishing to learn more about plants, native peoples in British Columbia, or native uses of plants. The index includes all of the various plant names—common and scientific, family and species—mentioned in this book.

SOURCES OF INFORMATION

Many different references, both botanical and ethnographic, were consulted in the preparation of this book. The botanical descriptions and notations on the habitat and distribution of individual plant species were derived partially from personal observation, but mainly from information contained in various floristic works. Foremost among these was the five-volume flora edited by C. L. Hitchcock, *Vascular Plants of the Pacific Northwest* (1955–69). Others included: J. A. Calder and R. L. Taylor's *Flora of the Queen Charlotte Islands* (Part I) (1968); *Wild Flowers of British Columbia* (1973) by L. J. Clark; *Flora of Southern British Columbia* (1915) by J. K. Henry and its supplement (1947) by J. W. Eastham; *Flora of Alaska* (1968) by E. Hultén; and the British Columbia Provincial Museum Handbooks on *The Ferns and Fern-allies of British Columbia; The Heather Family (Ericaceae) of British Columbia; The Lily Family (Liliaceae) of British Columbia; Guide to Common Seaweeds of British Columbia; Some Common Mosses of British Columbia; The Rose Family (Rosaceae) of British Columbia; Pocket Guide to the Trees and Shrubs of British Columbia; The Pea Family (Leguminosae) of British Columbia; The Figwort Family (Scrophulariaceae) of British Columbia;* and *Food Plants of British Columbia Indians Part 1/Coastal Peoples and Part 2/Interior Peoples* Handbooks 12, 19, 25, 27, 28, 30, 31, 32, 33, 34, and 36 (respectively).

Information on the uses of plants by Indian peoples was contributed largely by elder members of contemporary Indian communities, named individually in the Preface. Their knowledge came from personal experiences and from past conversations with the elders of previous generations. Many literature sources were also consulted. Some of the most significant are: Franz Boas' *Ethnology of the Kwakiutl* (1921); E. Steedman's "Ethnobotany of the Thompson Indians of British Columbia" (1930) based on the notes of James Teit; Teit's *The Salishan Tribes of the Western Plateaus* (1928); *The Thompson Indians* (1900); *The Lillooet Indians* (1906); and *The Shuswap* (1901); Rev. A. G. Morice's "Notes Archaeological, Industrial and Sociological on the Western Dénés" (Carrier and Chilcotin) (1893); and S. McNeary's *The Traditional Economic and Social Life of the Niska of British Columbia* (1974). Considerable information on plant materials used by various Salishan groups of the Coast and the Interior was provided by R. Bouchard and D. Kennedy of the British Columbia Indian Language Project, Victoria, from their own field research. Kennedy and Bouchard have compiled a number of excellent papers on the utilization of fish and marine life by various Salish groups. These include discussions of plant materials used in fishing technologies and have been very helpful. Information on plant technology of the Indians of western Washington was obtained from E. Gunther's *The Ethnobotany of Western Washington* (1945). Descriptions of plant materials used by the Flathead and Kootenay peoples of western Montana were obtained from J. Hart's *Plant Taxonomy of the Salish and Kootenai Indians of Western Montana* (1974), and of those employed by the Blackfoot of Alberta from A. Johnston's "Blackfoot Indian Utilization of the Flora of the Northwestern Great Plains" (1970) and J. Hellson and M. Gadd's *Ethnobotany of the Blackfoot Indians* (1974). These references and many others are enumerated in detail in the Reference List.

THE PHYSICAL ENVIRONMENT

No province in Canada has greater topographic, climatic, and biological diversity than British Columbia. From the rugged coastline on the Pacific to the steep, jagged peaks of the Rocky Mountains in the east, the landscape is a continuously changing series of hills, mountains, plateaus, plains, valleys, canyons, marshes, muskegs, lakes and rivers. Annual preciptation of 250 cm (about 100 in.) or more on the west coast of Vancouver Island contrasts startlingly with the semi-desert conditions in parts of the southern Interior, where combined rain and snow barely exceeds 25 cm (10 in.) a year. The mild, Mediterranean-like climate of south-eastern Vancouver ·Island, which can support blooming flowers even in mid-winter, is far removed from the chilling subarctic temperatures of the central and northern Interior, where the mean temperature for the month of January may be less than −18°C (0°F).

In a region characterized by so much variety it is difficult to summarize the essential geographical and biological features in a few pages. However, it is the very diversity of landscape, climate, and vegetation which has allowed the native utilization of so many different plants in such a variety of ways. Thus, an understanding of the environmental setting of the book is of major importance.

PHYSIOGRAPHY

The two predominating physiographic features of the Province, enclosing all but the northeastern corner, are the Coast Mountain range on the west and the Rocky Mountains on the east. The Coast range includes the Coast and Cascade Mountains. They and the Rockies are part of the great system of mountains known as the Cordillera extending in a north-south direction along the entire western side of North and South America. The northeastern corner of the Province, east of the Rockies, is part of the great Interior Plains region.

Between the Coast and Rocky Mountain ranges is an alternating mountain and plateau system including the extensive Interior Plateau and the Columbia Mountains, in the south, and the Stikine Plateau and the Omineca, Hazelton, Skeena, and Cassiar Mountains, in the north. The Columbia range has four major subdivisions: the Purcell, Selkirk, Monashee, and Cariboo mountains.

A multitude of lakes and rivers with their associated valleys, flood plains, marshes, canyons, gorges, and benchlands are encompassed within the mountain-plateau system, separating individual mountain ranges and cutting through the plateaus. Immediately west of the Rocky Mountains is a long, straight valley, known as the Rocky Mountain Trench. About three to sixteen kilometres wide, it flanks the Rockies throughout their range. Most of the rivers west of the Rocky Mountains flow southward and westward to the Pacific, transecting the Coast range. The land east of the Rockies drains northward into the Arctic Ocean.

The Coast mountain range extends onto Vancouver Island and the Queen Charlotte Islands. The coastline of both these islands and the Mainland is for the most part rocky and indented, with a multitude of steep, narrow fjords and inlets. There are, however, occasional shallow bays and wide stretches of sandy beach. Lowland Coastal plains occur along the east coast of Vancouver Island and the northeastern corner of Graham Island on the Queen Charlottes. At the estuaries of the major rivers, such as the Fraser, are fertile alluvial floodplains and deltas.

The native peoples of the Province were not, for the most part, montane. They preferred for their habitations the seacoast with its bays, inlets, and estuaries, and the Interior plateaus, benchlands, and river valleys. The ocean, and the Interior waterways, were a primary source of food and a major means of transportation. The uplands were seldom ventured into except for hunting, food gathering, or occasional trading expeditions. The steep, rugged slopes and snow-covered peaks were major barriers to travel and communication and must certainly account, in part, for the great linguistic and cultural variation among British Columbia Indians. Despite the cultural differences, the various native technologies were by-and-large those of lowland water-oriented societies. Canoes—dugout craft on the Coast and birch-bark or dugout vessels in the Interior—were important pieces of equipment, as were the various implements required for fishing and marine hunting—paddles, nets, lines, weirs, harpoons, and spears. Thus, it can be said that the very nature of the landscape had some effect in determining how plants were used in native technologies.

CLIMATE

Climatically, British Columbia lies within the North Temperate Zone. The weather patterns are largely controlled by air masses and pressure systems moving across the Province in a west to east direction. However, these basic patterns are modified considerably by topography, altitude, and latitude, thus no two localities within the Province can be said to have exactly the same climatic conditions.

In general, five major climatic regions can be delineated. The first includes eastern Vancouver Island, the Strait of Georgia, and the Fraser River delta. Lying within the rain-shadow area produced by the mountains of the Olympic Peninsula and Vancouver Island, and in a maritime environment, this region is characterized by dry, cool summers and humid, mild winters. The climate in this area is often termed "Mediterranean" because of its similarity to that of western California and southern Europe.

The second major zone includes the rest of the Pacific coast—western and northern Vancouver Island, the Queen Charlotte Islands, and the western slopes of the Coast Mountains on the mainland. The precipitation here is heavy and the temperatures, at least in the lower altitudes, are moderate, due to the oceanic influence. Gales, especially "southwesters," are frequent during the winter.

The third climatic region includes the Interior Plateau of central and southern British Columbia east of the Coast Mountains. It lies within the rain shadow of the Coast range, and this, combined with other factors, makes it one of the driest areas in Canada. Without the marine influence, the winter temperatures are considerably colder than on the Coast, and the summer temperatures significantly hotter.

The fourth region encompasses the Columbia Mountain system and the Rocky Mountains, along with their associated valleys and the Rocky Mountain Trench. Except for a few sheltered valleys, such as in the western Trench area, this region is more humid than the Interior Plateau; the Pacific air masses in ascending the mountain slopes precipitate more moisture than when passing over the Plateau. The topographic complexity yields a wide variety of local climates, but in general, the higher altitude and continental influence result in a more extreme temperature regime than on the Coast. This region, except for the dry, rain-shadow areas, is known as the "Interior wet belt."

The fifth climatic zone includes all of the northern Interior of British Columbia above about 53°N. latitude. Most of this area is subject to continental influences throughout the year, although the southern part, around Prince George, is often invaded by the relatively moist, mild Pacific air masses, which tend to moderate the harsh climatic conditions of the north, as well as produce higher precipitation levels. Most of the northern region is characterized by light to moderate precipitation, long, cold winters, and short, warm summers.

These climatic zones and the topographic information given previously are described in detail in the introductory section of the British Columbia volume of the Gazetteer of Canada, prepared by the former Department of Lands and Forests, British Columbia (1953 edition).

Like the topography, the climate in different areas of the Province had a significant effect, both direct and indirect, on the types of plants used in native technologies and the ways in which they were employed. For example, the various architectural styles and materials used for dwellings and the different types of clothing worn in the various regions were certainly influenced by climatic patterns. In the rainy coastal zone, the large cedar-board houses and woven cedar-bark clothing were eminently suitable, while in the Interior, semi-subterranean huts and skin clothing were more appropriate for the severe winter weather, while temporary "teepees" or mat huts and plant-fibre clothing served in the hot summer months, although some of the more nomadic peoples used skin teepees for shelter throughout the year. Various implements such as snowshoes, widely used in the Interior, were also directly related to climate.

BIOLOGY

Indirectly, the climate has a major effect in determining the type of vegetation which occurs in an area and hence on the plants which were available as materials to the peoples of any region. At least eleven different vegetation zones, technically known as "biogeoclimatic" zones, are distinguished within the Province on the basis of geography, climate, and frequency and abundance of various plant species. These zones coincide generally with the five major climatic zones outlined previously, but are more specific, reflecting the effects of elevation and latitude on climate and vegetation.

On the Coast, three zones are delineated in the area frequented by native peoples: the Coastal Douglas-fir Zone, occurring on the leeward side of Vancouver Island, the Gulf Islands and the lowland areas of the adjacent Mainland; the Coastal Western Hemlock Zone, along the windward side of Vancouver Island, on the Queen Charlotte Islands and on the Mainland of the Strait of Georgia above 90 m (300 ft) elevation and northward along the entire Mainland coast below a range of about 1 000 m (3,300 ft) in the south to 320 m (1,000 ft) in the north; and the Mountain Hemlock Zone, above the Coastal Western Hemlock Zone at subalpine elevations [between about 915 and 1 700 m (3,000 and 5,500 ft) in the south and between about 320 and 610 m (1,000 and 2,000 ft) on the Alaskan Panhandle].

The Coastal Douglas-fir Zone, with an average precipitation of 66 to 152 cm (26 to 60 in.), is characterized by the presence of the coastal variety of Douglas-fir (*Pseudotsuga menziesii* var. *menziesii*), and a number of other tree species—Pacific madrone (*Arbutus menziesii*), Garry oak (*Quercus garryana*), lodgepole pine (*Pinus contorta*) grand fir (*Abies grandis*), broad-leafed maple (*Acer macrophyllum*), and red alder (*Alnus rubra*). The Coastal Western Hemlock Zone, with an average annual precipitation of 165 to 665 cm (65 to 262 in.), supports, as well as western hemlock (*Tsuga heterophylla*), western red cedar (*Thuja plicata*), Sitka spruce (*Picea sitchensis*), amabilis or silver fir (*Abies amabilis*), and red alder, also common in the Coastal Douglas-fir Zone. The Mountain Hemlock Zone, occurring at a higher altitude, has an average annual precipitation of 178 to 432 cm (70 to 170 in.), much of it in the form of snow. Trees associated with this zone are mountain hemlock (*Tsuga mertensiana*), yellow cedar (*Cha-*

maecyparis nootkatensis), silver fir, and occasionally subalpine fir (*Abies lasiocarpa*).

The Interior vegetation zones are as follows: the Engelmann Spruce—Subalpine Fir Zone, at subalpine elevations throughout about 1 200 to 2 200 m (4,000 to 7,200 ft) in the south and 1 000 to 1 600 m (3,280 to 5,150 ft) in the north; the Interior Douglas-fir Zone, in the southern Interior Plateau and the Columbia and Kootenay Valleys at moderate elevations between about 300 and 1 350 m (1,000 and 4,500 ft), but varying with location; the Ponderosa Pine—Bunchgrass Zone, of the driest lowlands of the Interior Plateau and Columbia Valley, south of 51°30′N. latitude, between 270 and 750 m (900 and 2,500 ft); the Interior Western Hemlock Zone, within the region of the Interior wet belt between the Rockies and the Monashee Mountains, south of 54°N. latitude, from 360 to 1 260 m (1,200 to 4,200 ft); the Cariboo Aspen—Lodgepole Pine—Douglas-fir Zone, occurring in the northern Interior Plateau, between 510 and 900 m (1,700 and 3,000 ft) elevation; the Sub-boreal Spruce Zone of north-central British Columbia, from 53° to 57°N. latitude, between 330 and 840 m (1,100 and 2,800 ft) elevation; and the Boreal White and Black Spruce Zone, in the far northern part of the Province, above 54°40′N. latitude, from 165 to 840 m (550 to 2,800 ft) elevation.

The eleventh zone, the Alpine Tundra, occurs in the mountains above the tree line both on the Coast and in the Interior, but was seldom encountered by the native peoples.

As would be expected, the most characteristic trees of the moist, upland Engelmann Spruce—Subalpine Fir Zone, where precipitation averages 41 to 183 cm (16 to 72 in.) annually, most of it in the form of snow, are Engelmann spruce (*Picea engelmannii*) and subalpine fir (*Abies lasiocarpa*). Others include lodgepole pine (*Pinus contorta*), whitebark pine (*Pinus albicaulis*), and alpine larch (*Larix lyallii*). All of these are cold-tolerant species. Common trees of the Interior Douglas-fir Zone, with an average annual precipitation of 36 to 56 cm (14 to 22 in.), are, besides Interior Douglas-fir (*Pseudotsuga menziesii* var. *glauca*) itself, ponderosa pine (*Pinus ponderosa*), white pine (*Pinus monticola*), lodgepole pine, grand fir (*Abies grandis*), western larch

19

(*Larix occidentalis*), trembling aspen (*Populus tremuloides*), black cottonwood (*Populus balsamifera* ssp. *trichocarpa*), Rocky Mountain maple (*Acer glabrum*), and western white birch (*Betula papyrifera*).

In the dry Ponderosa Pine—Bunchgrass Zone, with an average annual precipitation of only 19 to 36 cm (7.4 to 14 in.), ponderosa pine and Interior Douglas-fir predominate, along with a number of shrubs, including big sagebrush (*Artemisia tridentata*) and greasewood, or antelope bush (*Purshia tridentata*). The Interior Western Hemlock Zone, with 56 to 170 cm (22 to 67 in.) annual precipitation, is characterized by western hemlock (*Tsuga heterophylla*), western larch, grand fir, lodgepole pine, white pine, black cottonwood, trembling aspen, and western white birch. Trees of the Cariboo Aspen—Lodgepole pine—Douglas-fir Zone, where annual precipitation averages 36 to 56 cm (14 to 22 in.), are, aside from the three the zone is named after, white spruce (*Picea glauca*) and in the northern part, black spruce (*Picea mariana*). The Subboreal Spruce and Boreal White and Black Spruce Zones are cold and fairly dry with an annual precipitation of 40 to 64 cm (16 to 25 in.) and 30 to 58 cm (12 to 23 in.) respectively. Plant growth is poor because of the short growing season. The major trees include white and black spruce, subalpine fir, alpine larch, and lodgepole pine.

The reader can learn more about the biogeoclimatic zones of the Province and the vegetation associated with them by consulting V. J. Krajina's "Ecology of Forest Trees of British Columbia" in *Ecology of Western North America* (1969). Many of the plants mentioned in this book are restricted to one or two of these zones, or at least grow more abundantly within them. Hence some native peoples had better access to certain species than other groups. Those living on the Coast and in areas of the southern Interior where western red cedar was abundant were fortunate indeed. However, the Interior peoples in their turn had access to certain species, such as western white birch, which were not generally available on the Coast. The ingenuity and inventiveness of the people themselves in adapting the vegetative materials at hand to suit their individual requirements is remarkable. The bent cedar-board boxes of the Coastal peoples and the sewn birch-bark vessels of the Interior groups served the same general function, but the materials themselves and the ways in which they were handled were strikingly different.

Trading overcame some of the discrepancies in available plant materials, but in general the native peoples were limited to the plants which grew in their particular areas. In every case it must be stated that they did a superb job in utilizing them to fullest advantage.

The fauna of British Columbia—the birds, mammals, reptiles, amphibians, fish, and invertebrates—cannot be discussed here in detail, but it must be mentioned that the animals are as variable and diverse as the vegetation. Their distribution is largely affected by climate, topography, and vegetation, and their influence on native lifestyles was immense. They provided the greatest source of food, the contribution of vegetable foods being secondary in all cases, and as such they had a profound effect on the types of implements and equipment used by native peoples. Many of the tools made from plant products—bows and arrows, harpoons, spears, and nets, to name a few—were directly related to the quest for animal foods, and many others, such as canoes, grease boxes, and drying racks, were at least partially connected with hunting and fishing activities. Animal products were generally not as important technologically as vegetative products, with the exception of in the northern Interior, where vegetative diversity is very poor. However, skins, sinew, bone, antler, horn, animal fat, feathers, and porcupine quills were all utilized to some extent.

Together the plants and animals of the Province provided sustenance for more than 70,000 people within nearly thirty different language and cultural groups. Within their given environment the technologies of these people were highly specialized and superbly adapted—a credit to their skill, knowledge, and ingenuity.

BRITISH COLUMBIA INDIANS AND THEIR USE OF PLANTS AS MATERIALS

NATIVE PEOPLES IN BRITISH COLUMBIA

The Indian groups of British Columbia are distinguished on the basis of language as follows: On the Coast—Straits Salish (Saanich, Songish, Klallam, Sooke, and Semiahmoo dialects); Halkomelem (Nanaimo, Chemainus, Cowichan, and Upper and Lower Stalo dialects); Squamish; Sechelt; Comox (Island Comox, Homalko, Sliammon, and Klahuse dialects); Bella Coola; Nootka (Northern, Central, and Southern or Nitinat dialects); Southern Kwakiutl; Central Kwakiutl (also known as Bella Bella or Heiltsuk); Northern Kwakiutl (or Haisla); Coast Tsimshian; and Haida (Masset and Skidegate dialects); and in the Interior—Thompson (Upper and Lower dialects); Lillooet (Upper and Lower dialects); Okanagan (Northern Okanagan, Lakes, and Similkameen dialects); Shuswap (Northern, Kamloops, and Chase dialects); Kootenay (also spelled Kutenai—Upper and Lower dialects); Niska (often spelled Nishga); Gitksan; Tlingit (Inland Tlingit dialect only); Chilcotin; Carrier (Upper, Lower, and Babine dialects); Sekani; Tahltan; Kaska; Slave; Beaver; and Tagish (recently largely replaced by the Inland Tlingit). The territories occupied by these peoples are shown on the accompanying map.

Some of these languages are quite closely related; others are as remote from each other as English and Swahili. The languages spoken by the southern Coastal peoples—Straits Salish, Halkomelem, Squamish, Sechelt, Comox, and also Bella Coola—form part of the Coastal division of the Salish Language Family, while those spoken by the south-central Interior peoples—Thompson, Lillooet, Okanagan, and Shuswap—form part of the Interior division of the Salish Language Family. On the Coast the languages spoken by the various Kwakiutlan groups and the Nootka are classed together in the Wakashan Language Family. The languages spoken by the peoples of the central-northern Interior, including Chilcotin, Carrier, Sekani, Tahltan, Kaska, Tagish, Slave, and Beaver, form part of the Athapaskan Family of Languages. This family is in turn considered to be broadly related to the Tlingit language of the

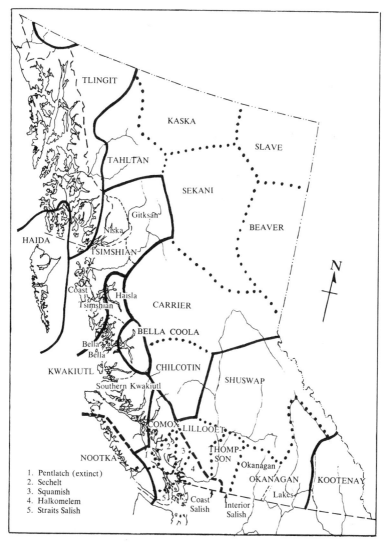

Map of British Columbia Indian groups, linguistic subdivisions (*after* Duff 1964)

British Columbia Interior and Coastal Alaska. The language of the Haida on the Queen Charlotte Islands and some of the Alaskan coastal islands is, according to the most up-to-date research, best considered a linguistic isolate. The languages of the Coast Tsimshian, Niska, and Gitksan peoples form part of the Penutian Language Family. In southeastern British Columbia, the language of the Kootenay peoples is believed to be, like Haida, a linguistic isolate.

The reader can obtain more detailed information on the general linguistic affiliations of British Columbia native peoples from a book entitled *The Indian History of British Columbia, Vol. 1, The Impact of the White Man,* published in 1964 by the British Columbia Provincial Museum.

Whereas each group is culturally as well as linguistically unique, many of them, even when completely unrelated linguistically, share common cultural traits, and can be categorized at a general level into major cultural units. All of the Coastal peoples, from the Straits Salish of southern Vancouver Island to the Haida and Tsimshian in the north, belong to the Northwest Coast Culture Area, which also encompasses the coastal peoples of Washington, Oregon, and northern California, as well as the Coastal Tlingit of Alaska. It is characterized by a number of distinctive features, including a marine fishing and water-oriented economy, with special dependence on the Pacific salmon, and extensive use, formerly, of the western red cedar for construction of dugout canoes, plank houses, and other wooden objects. The bark fibre of both red cedar and yellow cedar was commonly employed for making clothing, ropes, blankets, and mats.

In the Interior, two main cultural units are represented. The Salishan peoples of the Interior Plateau and the Kootenay people of eastern British Columbia are classed together with the various Salishan peoples and the Nez Percés of central and eastern Washington, Idaho, and western Montana, in the Plateau Culture Area. These groups, especially the Kootenays, possessed many of the cultural traits of the Plains Indians, but were generally less nomadic. The major food of the Plateau Culture Area peoples was the Pacific salmon, which came in great numbers every year up the Fraser and

Columbia River systems to spawn. They used a great variety of plant materials, including some plant fibre for clothing, Indian hemp for rope and line, and split cedar root and birch bark for basketry.

The various Athapaskan groups of central and northern British Columbia are classed, along with the peoples of central Alaska, the Yukon, the western Northwest Territories, and northern Alberta and Saskatchewan, in the Sub-Arctic Culture Area. The peoples in this region were widely scattered semi-nomads who travelled by birch-bark or spruce-bark canoe or, in winter, by snowshoes, and depended heavily on the meat of large game animals such as moose and caribou for their food. They used some plant materials, such as birch bark, but in general their clothing and shelter were provided by animal products.

The Interior groups bordering the Coastal zone—notably the Lower Lillooet, Lower Thompson, Inland Tlingit, Gitksan, and Niska (this last group actually borders the ocean on part of its territory)—are culturally transitional, sharing many of the cultural features of the Northwest Coast Culture Area. They had access to many Coastal plant materials not readily available to other Interior groups, and at the same time were able to utilize many typically interior plant products.

A general summary of the characteristic traits of the cultural areas mentioned in this section can be found in *Indians of North America* (1961) by Harold E. Driver. The writings of Boas, Swanton, Drucker, Barnett, Teit, Chamberlain, Emmons, and Morice, all listed in the References, provide specific information on the cultural features of individual groups.

It is important, when observing and comparing the use of plant materials in different regions of the Province, to understand cultural differences as well as vegetational ones. As a general rule, plants of major technological importance were utilized by native peoples throughout the area of their distribution. There are exceptions to this rule, of course. The so-called "ironwood" or oceanspray, was widely valued for its hard, strong wood by the peoples of the southern Coast and the Interior, being employed mainly for making digging sticks, but apparently was not used by the Bella Coola, even though it grows in their area. However, plants such as western red cedar, western yew, western white birch, Indian hemp, and red alder were employed almost universally within their ranges. The ways in which these plants were used, however, and the methods of preparation applied were much more variable, and seem more related to cultural variations among different Indian groups. The use of plants of lesser technological importance also varies considerably, being more contingent on cultural practices than on the distribution of the species.

PLANT MATERIALS USED

Plants were employed in many different capacities in British Columbia Indian cultures. Woods were used for carving implements, containers, and canoes, for construction, and as fuel for cooking, heating, and smoking foods. Sheets of bark were utilized for making containers and canoes, for lining underground food caches, and as roofing. Bark, stem, leaf, and root fibres were made into twine, ropes, fishing lines and nets, baskets, mats, and clothing. Additionally, plants and plant products were used as bedding, floor covering, and lining for berry baskets, drying racks, and steaming pits, as storage vessels and water conductors, and as herring-spawn collectors, soapberry beaters, infant diapers, wound dressings, abrasives, and tinder to start fires, as well as for making paints, dyes, and tanning agents, glues, animal poisons, insect repellents, scents, soaps and cleansing agents, decorations, and toys and recreational objects. They were also employed as biological indicators for various seasonal and climatological events.

In this section some examples are given of the types of plants utilized in these roles. The list is certainly not exhaustive, but it is hoped that the reader will at least gain from it a feeling for the great versatility of the vegetation around him and for the ingenuity of the native people in adapting the plants for their use.

For general all-round utility, few woods could match the versatile western red cedar. Soft, easily split and worked, but durable and rot-resistant, this wood was highly valued throughout its range, but especially on the Coast, where it grows abundantly and to a tremendous height and girth. House planks and posts, canoes, totem poles, and innumerable smaller items were traditionally hewn from red cedar wood. It was also an excellent fuel, burning quickly with a hot flame. The flexible young branches, or withes, were widely used as well, especially for making rope and line.

In the Interior, cottowood had some of the same characteristics as cedar and was commonly used to make dugout canoes and as a fuel. The dead wood and dried roots were valued for making the hearth and drill to start friction fires. Many other woods of both trees and shrubs were employed, most in more or less specialized ways. Western yew, a hard, resilient wood, was used to make such items as bows, wedges, digging sticks, harpoon and spear shafts, and adze handles. Wild crabapple was considered a good substitute for yew in making these implements. Yellow cedar, flowering dogwood, and Rocky Mountain maple were considered good woods for making bows, and the hardwood shrubs oceanspray, or "ironwood", and mock-orange were frequently used to make digging sticks and smaller items such as combs, needles, and arrows. Saskatoon wood was used throughout the Interior for making arrows, and also to make drying racks, sweat house frames, and canoe and basket frames. Red-osier dogwood branches were also used to make frames and basket rims. Vine maple and Rocky Mountain maple were often used to make snowshoe frames, while broad-leafed maple was employed for spindle whorls and paddles. Red alder, a soft, light-coloured, even-grained wood, was utilized for carving masks and dishes of all sizes and was valued as a fuel, especially for smoking meat and fish. Lodgepole pine and western hemlock trees were used to make poles for many purposes. Ponderosa pine was used in construction and even occasionally for dugout canoes in the southern Interior. Lodgepole pine, ponderosa pine, and Pacific willow were all employed in given areas as the hearth and drill in making friction fires. The knots and roots of Douglas-fir, western hemlock, and Sitka spruce were molded into cod and halibut hooks on the Coast, while in the Interior, Douglas-fir branches were used to make dipnet hoops.

Tree barks were almost as useful as woods. Douglas-fir bark had the reputation in many areas of being an excellent fuel. Almost everyone is familiar with the widespread use of birch bark for making canoes and baskets, not only in the British Columbia

Interior, but all across the country. Other barks, including Engelmann spruce, subalpine fir, grand fir and white pine, could be used similarly. Cottonwood bark was used to make storage buckets and to line underground food caches, and sheets of red cedar bark were made into buckets as well as used as roofing by some Coastal groups. The fibrous inner bark of both red cedar and yellow cedar was cut into thin strips and used to make capes, skirts, bodices, hats, mats, blankets, baskets, rope and twine, and, shredded, for baby diapers, napkins, towelling, and tinder. The tough, waterproof bark of the bitter, or wild, cherry was pulled off the tree in horizontal, or spirally-cut, strips and used to wrap the joints of implements, particularly those to be used in or near water, such as harpoons, fish-spears, and fish-hooks. It was also used to imbricate patterns on coiled baskets, being a beautiful varnished red colour and dyeing easily to jet black. Several other bark fibres were used, particularly in the Interior, for making ropes, bags, and clothing. These included various willow species, silverberry, white clematis, and big sagebrush.

Other plant fibres were also employed. Stem fibres of such herbaceous species as Indian hemp, spreading dogbane, stinging nettle, and fireweed were spun into twine, fishing lines, and nets. The strong, pliable stems of the bull kelp were used to make fishing lines and anchor lines by most Coastal groups. The fibrous leaves of grasses and grass-like plants, including common reedgrass, rye-grass, bear-grass (actually a lily), sea-grass, sedges, and cat-tail, as well as the stems of tule, were used to weave baskets, bags, and mats, or to imbricate and trim these articles. Fibrous roots, such as those of red cedar and Sitka spruce were split lengthwise into thin strands and woven into baskets, hats, and other articles, and used for binding, tying and "sewing" the seams of wood and bark containers. Often different kinds of fibres were used in combination, being spun together or used in different parts of a basket or other item.

Cat-tail and tule mats were commonly used as bedding, but boughs of conifers such as Douglas-fir, subalpine fir, grand fir, lodgepole pine, and even spruce, when not next to the skin, were also used. The woolly seed-fluff of cat-tail, cottonwood, and fireweed was used as stuffing for cloth mattresses and pillows. Sword-fern and bracken fern fronds, grasses, willow and red-osier dog-wood branches, and conifer boughs were used as matting to cover the floors of summer and winter houses and sweat lodges. Various types of vegetation, including skunk cabbage leaves, salal branches, seaweeds, and mosses, were used to line steam-cooking pits, pro-viding moisture and keeping the food clean. The large, flat leaves of the skunk cabbage were ideal for drying berries on and served to line berry baskets and as makeshift berry and drinking containers as well. Other broad leaves of plants such as thimbleberry, cow parsnip, and broad-leafed maple, were used for these purposes when skunk cabbage was not available. The hollow stipes of the bull kelp were used to mold yew-wood bows and wooden fish hooks, and also served as water conductors in steaming pits and as sound carriers to create special effects during winter dances. The floats and stems were cured and used as storage containers for grease and oil. Hollowed out elderberry stems and curled birch-bark tubes were used as urine conduits in baby carriers, and hollow grass stems and cow parsnip and angelica stems were sometimes used as drinking straws and underwater breathing tubes.

Along the Coast, the boughs of western hemlock and red cedar were placed in the ocean during the herring spawning season to collect herring eggs, a great delicacy in native diet. Marine plants, including eel-grass and sea-grass and some types of kelp were also used; some were eaten along with the spawn, while others were stripped away and discarded.

Several plants were used by various British Columbia Indian groups in the preparation of "Indian ice-cream," a favourite whipped confection made from soapberries (*Shepherdia canaden-sis*). The Thompson used "timbergrass," both to dry the berries on and to whip them. Thimbleberry leaves, broad-leafed maple leaves, salal branches, and beaters made from Rocky Mountain maple bark were some of the other botanical objects used as soapberry beaters.

The use of shredded cedar bark for diapers, napkins, and towelling has already been mentioned. Several other plant prod-ucts were valued for their absorptive properties and were used similarly. These include "old man's beard" lichen, black tree lichen (also used to make shoes and clothing in the Interior), sphagnum moss and other mosses, cat-tail, fireweed, and cottonwood seed fluff, the inner bark of some willows, and dry, rotten aspen wood.

The silicon-impregnated cell walls of the horsetails or scouring rushes in the genus *Equisetum* made them ideal as abrasives, for smoothing and finishing carved objects of wood or stone. They were employed for this purpose throughout the Province. Certain plant products were especially suitable as tinder for starting friction fires or for transporting or storing embers in a "slow match." Spiny wood fern roots, the inner fibres of bracken fern rhizomes, shredded cedar bark, big sagebrush bark, and bracket fungus tissue were all utilized in this capacity.

Many plants were used to make dyes, stains, and paints. Foremost among these was red alder, which yields, depending on the treatment, colours ranging from bright red to orange to dark brown. It was used to dye cedar bark, basket materials, and fishing line. Indian paint fungus yields a red pigment as well, and was used mainly as a face paint. Other red pigments were made from western larch gum and stoneseed roots. Western hemlock bark was sometimes used as a reddish-brown dye, and was also employed as a tanning agent. Certain berries, such as blackcap, wild raspberry, salal, and black twinberry, were mashed and used as purple stains. Hazelnut shoots and larkspur flowers were employed in some areas as blue colourings. Yellow was obtained from the inner bark and roots of Oregon grape and from the bright yellow-green wolf lichen. Sometimes they were mixed. Cottonwood bud resin was used as a yellow paint and as a base for paints of other colours as well. Grass, and green algae, in both wood and water, provided green pigments, charcoal and organic earth were commonly used to produce black; and flowering dogwood bark and grand fir bark also yielded a black pigment. Recently some groups used water in which rusty nails had been soaking to dye cedar bark black. Several different tree barks were used as tanning agents. The Thompson and Sechelt used species of bracket fungi, alone or mixed with deer brains, for this purpose.

The heated mucilage from the inside of prickly pear cactus stems was used by some groups as fixative for paints and stains.

Tree pitch from species such as cottonwood, Sitka spruce, lodgepole pine, western hemlock, and subalpine fir provided natural glues for such tasks as sticking parts of implements together, fastening bitter cherry bark wrapping in place, fixing poultices and wound dressings, and waterproofing canoes and baskets. Sometimes pitch was mixed with animal grease and rubbed on the surfaces of implements to protect them.

The roots of Rocky Mountain juniper, stoneseed, and stinging nettle were all used in the southern Interior as arrow poisons. A plant in the celery family, chocolate tips, was used as a fish poison by the Okanagan, and was also used as an insecticide for livestock. Vanilla-leaf and some of the strong-smelling plants in the aster family, notably the big sagebrush and its relatives in the genus *Artemisia,* were used in solution or burned as a smudge for insect repellents, to eliminate lice and bedbugs from bedding, and to disperse flying insect pests such as mosquitoes. The Artemisias and a number of other plants were valued for their aromatic scent and were used in sachets and as incense and fumigants. Some of the most noteworthy are Rocky Mountain juniper, grand fir and subalpine fir, sweetgrass, and Indian consumption plant.

Soaps and shampoos were made from, among others, cottonwood ashes and inner bark, birch leaves, mock-orange leaves and flowers, and white clematis leaves. Hemlock and grand fir boughs were used by some Coastal peoples to make special dance costumes for shamans and initiates. The fruits or seeds of a number of plants, including stoneseed, silverberry, wild rose, cactus, and Pacific madrone, were used as beads for necklaces and decorations on clothing, especially by women.

The Indian children of the Province, like children everywhere, were able to amuse themselves with the simplest of playthings. They liked to step on the bladders of sea wrack and other seaweeds to make them pop, and to squirt water from the elongated sacs of *Halosaccion,* another marine alga. Nootka children dried the floats of the giant kelp and threw them on the fire to make them explode "like firecrackers." Squamish and other south Coastal children played an endurance game with sword-fern fronds, pulling off the leaflets one at a time and saying "pála" with each one to see who could pull off the most in one breath. Bella Coola girls played a game with Indian paintbrush flowers; one girl held the flower while girls on the opposite team sang a song and tried to make her laugh or smile. Okanagan children played a "wishbone" game with little hooked stems of the wild buckwheat plant. Children in many parts of the Province made blowguns from hollowed elderberry stems or cow parsnip stems, using pieces of kelp or other vegetation as ammunition.

Adults, too, used many plants and plant products in their recreational activities. For example, Okanagan men played a type of throwing game using as a target a spoked wheel made of Rocky Mountain juniper. They also played a pin and ball game, with red hawthorn spines as pins and tule stem balls. On the Coast a throwing game was played using salmonberry spears and bull kelp targets. The Nootka played a kind of hockey on the beach with "pucks" made of sections of dried kelp (*Laminaria*) stems. Tree fungi were used as balls in a Kwakiutl handball game and as targets in a Stalo bow-and-arrow game.

The use of plants as biological indicators was undoubtedly much more common and widespread than information available at present would indicate. Nevertheless there are some excellent examples of this type of use. According to Squamish lore, when the stinging nettle shoots were just appearing above the ground, it was the time when the seals were having their young. In Okanagan tradition, the blooming of the mock-oranges signified that the marmots were fat and ready to be hunted. When the larches turned yellow in the fall, pregnant female bears were entering their dens for the winter. Finally, the shimmering of trembling aspen leaves when there was no perceptible wind was taken as a sign of an impending storm.

Even with all the different ways of utilizing plants mentioned in this discussion, some of the technological uses of vegetation defy classification and categorization and can only be given as unique applications. Such is the use of living, growing white clematis vines by the Shuswap to straighten and strengthen implement handles and of prickly pear cactus plants placed around cache poles by the Okanagan to keep rodents and larger mammals away from food supplies.

HARVESTING PLANT MATERIALS

Most plant materials were harvested by hand or with the aid of simple tools. In the days before European contact trees were felled by chopping around the base with stone mauls and chisels of shell, horn, or stone, or with adzes of various types. Some groups also used controlled burning to fell trees, but more often windfallen logs were utilized or boards and half-logs were split from standing trees with the use of a series of graduated hardwood wedges. Iron was available even in pre-European times, but it was very rare. Naturally, with the introduction of larger quantities of iron for adzes, axes, and other tools, the harvesting of timber and plant materials in general was greatly facilitated.

Bark and bark-fibre was most easily gathered in late spring and early summer, when the running sap allowed the bark to separate easily from the underlying wood. Sheets of bark, such as that of western white birch, were obtained by making two horizontal cuts around the tree and one vertical cut between them, then peeling off the bark as a single unit. Bitter cherry bark was cut off the tree in thin horizontal, or spiral, strips. Red and yellow cedar bark was pulled off the trees in long vertical strips, as were most of the other bark fibres.

Fibrous stems and leaves were generally collected in late summer and fall when the plants were fully mature. The stems or leaves were cut, sorted, and bundled, then hung or spread to dry in the sun. Roots for basketry, tying, and binding were dug with wooden or iron digging sticks similar to the type used for harvesting edible roots. Trees widely spaced, growing in sandy or loamy soil were said to have the best roots. Long, straight roots of even thickness and with few side-branches were preferred. They could be gathered in any season, but late spring was said to be an ideal time because the bark peels off best then. The harvested roots were first cured by heating them over coals to prevent the woody tissue from darkening. After this the bark was removed and the

2

roots split and dried to be worked on later at the convenience of the harvester.

Most other plant materials were gathered fresh during the growing season. Some, such as those used for bedding, floor coverings, steaming pit linings, and insect repellents, were replenished frequently as they were needed. Others, including some dyestuffs, tinders, and cleansing agents, could be harvested in quantity, dried, and stored until needed.

As a general rule, the men were involved with the harvesting and construction of wood, as well as of larger sheets of bark for canoes. The women were usually responsible for collecting and preparing fibrous plant materials, such as cedar bark, and various leaves, stems, and roots for making baskets, mats, and clothing. However, if the fibres were to be used as fishing line and net, or in some way involved with fishing, hunting, or woodworking, the men might gather and process it as well. Other materials were gathered by men, women, or children, depending on the effort involved and on who would be using the final product.

Important plant materials such as cedar bark on the Coast or Indian hemp fibre in the Interior might be harvested during an outing of a day or several days by an entire family or a party of men or women in a village group. Such gathering expeditions were often combined with other activities in the same locality— hunting, fishing, digging edible roots, or picking berries. The materials could be processed in the field to the point where they would not spoil or deteriorate, then bundled and carried home to be worked on later in the season when the weather was too poor for travelling.

The gathering and preparation of the materials could be difficult and time consuming, but was undoubtedly made more enjoyable when undertaken by a group of people and turned into a social event. Songs, such as one sung by Haida women when pulling off cedar bark: "We want a long strip; go up high; go up high!", would certainly help ease the burden of the work.

Technologically important plants, like other natural resources within the territory of a village group, were considered to be the property of that group, and other peoples wishing to harvest them were obligated to ask permission from the village members. It is likely that individual members and families within a group could also own patches or stands of technological plants, as they could patches of edible plants in some areas.

According to native religious traditions, plants, like animals, were believed to have "souls" and to be capable of thought and feeling just as people are today. The need to utilize and exploit natural objects was recognized, but in general they were approached with reverence and respect and were never used wastefully or without due appreciation. This belief was reflected in the harvesting of plant materials, as can be seen in the following "prayer" by a Kwakiutl woman to a young cedar tree from which she is about to harvest the bark [from F. Boas' *The Religion of the Kwakiutl Indians* (1930)]:

PRAYER TO A YOUNG CEDAR

The woman goes into the woods to look for young cedar trees. As soon as she finds them, she picks out one that has no twists in the bark, and whose bark is not thick. She takes her hand adze and stands under the young cedar tree, and looking up to it, she prays, saying:

Look at me, friend,
I come to ask for your dress,
For you have come to take pity on us;
For there is nothing for which you cannot be used, . . .

For you are really willing to give us your dress,
I come to beg you for this,
Long-Life maker,
For I am going to make a basket for lily-roots out of you.

I pray, friend, do not feel angry
On account of what I am going to do to you;
And I beg you friend, to tell our friends about what I ask of you!

Take care friend!
Keep sickness away from me,
So that I may not be killed by sickness or in war,
O friend!

The Kwakiutl bark harvester was careful not to completely girdle a cedar tree, because this would kill the tree, and the nearby cedar trees would curse the person who did it. Present-day users of plant materials in British Columbia would do well to emulate this traditional respect of natural resources!

PREPARATION OF PLANT MATERIALS

The harvesting of plant materials must have been an arduous task at best, but in many cases it was only the beginning of a long, painstaking process leading ultimately to a beautifully finished product, whether it be a cedar-wood canoe, a tule mat, or a birch-bark basket. Imagine making a sweater with wool which you first had to go out and shear from the sheep, then wash and card, dye, spin, and finally knit. That would be approximately equivalent to the task of a native basketmaker or woodworker. Even the tiniest basket might take a day or more to complete; weaving a large basket would take many weeks, and carving a canoe might take an entire winter.

As mentioned earlier, woodworking activities were generally undertaken by the men in native cultures, while women were responsible for processing the various fibrous materials. Woodworking techniques involved the use of chisels, adzes, and knives for carving, wedges and mauls for splitting, and drills for gauging thickness and for sewing and pegging seams. Fire was also an important tool; controlled burning was often used to hollow out canoes and large feast dishes, and hardwoods, such as "ironwood," Saskatoon, mock-orange, and crabapple, were often "baked" over hot coals to make them even harder. Steam generated from red-hot rocks and damp vegetation, such as seaweed, was used to mold and bend woods in making such items as canoes, boxes, snowshoes, and fish-hooks. With careful work, steamed wood could actually be bent to an angle of 90 degrees or less, as was done to make the sides of kerfed cedar-wood boxes. The final step in making most wooden objects was to smooth and polish them. Shark or dogfish skin was often used for this purpose, but when it was not available horsetail stems were used.

Wooden objects, especially in the Northwest Coast area, were often decorated with precise, symmetrical, painted designs or relief carvings, usually of mythological themes or family or clan crests, many of zoological origin. Northwest Coast artifacts—not only wooden articles but also baskets—were frequently standardized in form and size. This was particularly true in the Kwakiutl culture, where every feast dish for two people, for example, or every clover-root digger or elderberry basket had virtually the same dimensions as every other. Finger-widths, hand-widths, arm-lengths, and pieces of string and rope were the usual measuring devices.

The preparation of fibres and fibrous materials required such tools as knives, beaters, and in the case of stem fibres, simple spindles. Sometimes a type of suspended warp loom was used for weaving robes and blankets of cedar bark, as it was for weaving mountain goat wool and other animal products. For sewing cat-tail and tule mats, long hardwood needles were used, and wooden "mat-creasers" to press the leaves or stems down around the needle, allowing it an easier passage and preventing the mat material from splitting. Awls and bone needles were used in the construction of birch-bark baskets and other items made of bark sheets. It can certainly be said, however, that by far the most important tools for the working of fibrous materials were the hands.

Sheets of bark were generally worked on as soon as they were harvested; otherwise they became too brittle. Red cedar bark sheets for roofing, for example, were flattened while still green by inserting sticks at intervals through the fibrous tissue, and weighting them with rocks until they dried. Birch bark and other barks used for canoes and baskets were cut and shaped according to the natural tendency of the bark to curl outwards, so that the inner surface of the bark formed the outside of the vessel. The seams were stitched with lengths of root and the top was bound to a light wooden frame which added strength and support. Special bark baskets were given a design by etching patterns into the bark surface, as well as by fancy edge stitching and the overlaying of materials such as porcupine quills.

Most other fibrous materials, after being processed to a certain point, could be dried and stored. When the worker was ready to use them they need only be soaked in warm water for a short time until they became flexible again. Stem fibres, such as those of stinging nettle and Indian hemp, were obtained by pounding and twisting the dried stems to remove the pithy tissue. The fibre was then spun into thread on the bare thigh or with the use of a long, hand-twirled spindle with a large hardwood or bone whorl as a flywheel to maintain an even tension. Lengths of fibre were spliced together during the spinning process to produce a continuous strand. Individual strands could be twisted or plaited together to form a 2-, 4-, or multi-ply twine or rope, suitable for fishing lines and nets, for sewing or twining mats and capes, or for binding implements.

Bark fibres and fibrous leaves, stems, and roots were used whole, split into pieces of uniform width, or, in the case of cedar bark, sometimes pounded into soft cottony strands. Various techniques of weaving and sewing these materials were applied, varying with the type of product desired, the type of plant used, and the cultural practises of individual groups. The Kwakiutl and Nootka specialized in weaving robes of yellow cedar bark with the aid of a simple loom. Long strands of the pounded bark were hung over a cord and twined together at intervals with double strands of tightly twisted red cedar bark or mountain goat wool. The Interior peoples used a similar technique to weave capes and clothing of such materials as silverberry bark or white clematis bark twined with Indian hemp string. The Coast Salish people made robes and blankets chiefly of mountain goat wool, duck and goose down, and the hair of small domesticated dogs, but they sometimes spun plant fibres, such as fireweed and cat-tail seed fluff, in with these materials. They used both twilled checker and twining weaves; in the latter red cedar-bark cord was often used as the weft material.

Cedar-bark mats and sometimes baskets and hats were woven by Coastal peoples in simple checkerwork and diagonal checkerwork styles. Often dyed bark strands were interspersed with the undyed elements to produce geometric patterns. Twilled designs were also made, especially on the borders. The Salish peoples of both the Coast and Interior traditionally made cat-tail and tule mats. The leaves or stems were laid side by side and sewn together with a long needle, or, in the case of tule, sometimes twined together at intervals with some type of fibre. The cut ends were often folded over and bound to keep them from tearing apart.

Most of the Northwest Coast baskets, except in the Salish areas, were made by twining techniques. Some were made with an open weave, to allow air circulation or draining of liquids, while others were woven extremely tightly. They were decorated by superimposing naturally or artificially coloured materials such as bear-grass and sea-grass and the stems of various true grasses in intricate patterns over the basic weave. The Nootka, Haida, and Tlingit of Alaska were especially proficient in fine, close, basket twining. They made flared waterproof hats by the same technique.

The Salishan peoples of the Province were specialists in coiled basketry, which involved sewing together spirals of flat or upright coils of fibrous materials such as split red cedar roots with flat strips of the same or a different material. The coils were sewn so closely and carefully that the underlying material was completely covered and only the evenly stitched outer layer was visible. As with twined baskets, coiled ones were decorated with imbricated designs. Often strips of natural red and black-dyed bitter cherry bark and straw-coloured grass leaves, such as of the common reed-grass, were used in the imbrication process.

Most other plant materials required little or no preparation. Plants for bedding, covering floors, lining steaming pits, drying racks, and berry baskets, collecting herring spawn, and whipping soapberries were used fresh. Processing involved such minor tasks as trimming large branches or removing the midribs of skunk cabbage leaves with a sharp knife. Bull kelp used for storing liquids and for water conduction could be employed fresh or, for greater durability, could be cured by alternate sun drying and soaking in fresh water. Materials for infant diapers, wound dressings, and tinder, were air dried before use and, in some cases, pounded to soften them. Horsetails for smoothing and finishing could be used fresh or dried. Tree pitch for glue was used fresh. Most of the plants used as insect repellents were burned while still green as a smudge or boiled to make a washing solution. Soaps and cleansing agents were used fresh, dried, or in solution, as were the various plants used for their scents. The latter were also burned as incense. Plants for animal poisons were usually steeped in water to obtain a solution. Most dyes and tanning agents were prepared by boiling the colouring material in water, sometimes with a urine mordant. Paints were usually obtained by pounding the dried plant matter to a powder and mixing this with ochre, fat, or resin. Stains were made by macerating fresh materials, such as berries, flowers, or leaves, and rubbing the pulp onto the object to be coloured.

In making almost any implement, container, or article of clothing the native artisan utilized a combination of different plant materials, all of which had to be gathered and processed. For example, a bow maker had to select, carve, and mold the appropriate wood, and prepare a strong bowstring, perhaps of Indian hemp fibre. He might bind the haft with bitter cherry bark, which would be fixed in place with a natural glue, such as tree pitch, and tied with more fibre. Finally, he might polish the wood with horsetail stems and decorate it with a vegetable paint or stain. A Nootka basket maker might use the inner bark of red cedar as a foundation for her product, one type of sedge for the bottom, another for the sides and top, bear-grass for the edging, and the same materials dyed, or other materials of different natural colours, for imbricating or weaving in designs. The potential for variation was limitless.

TRADING PLANT MATERIALS

Every group in the Province had access to a considerable variety of materially useful plants but of course some were much more highly prized than others. In areas where such plants did not occur naturally, they were often obtained by trade from neighbouring groups, either in the form of raw materials or as finished products. Often, too, the peoples of one group would be particularly skilled in constructing a certain type of product and would be able to trade it to neighbouring peoples even when the basic materials were just as readily available to the latter as the former.

The exchange of plant materials and other economic products took place at all levels—within family and village groups, between villages in the same language group, among the different language divisions on the Coast and in the Interior, and even between Coastal and Interior groups. Some groups, especially those in the transitional zone between the Coast and the Interior, acted as "middlemen," buying the products of one neighbouring group and reselling them to another. With the coming of the white man and the accompanying influx of new trade goods and improved transportation routes, the exchange of plant products became even more widespread.

Examples of the trading of raw materials are numerous. Beargrass, used for fine trimming and imbrication of baskets, was gathered by the peoples of the Olympic Peninsula and other parts of Washington, dried, tied in bundles, and traded to the Coast Salish and Nootka of Vancouver Island, who prized it greatly. Dyed and natural red cedar bark, and western yew, vine maple, and yellow cedar wood were transported from the Coast by the Lower Lillooet and traded to the Upper Lillooet in exchange for Indian hemp fibre, silverberry bark, and certain grasses used in basketry. These they then sold to the Squamish, Sechelt, and Comox peoples of the Coast. The Upper Lillooet sometimes sold yew wood and other Coastal materials, as well as mock-orange wood and some of the other products within their own territory to the Shuswap. Within Shuswap territory, materials such as red cedar roots for basketry were exchanged for salmon and other products at large tribal gatherings, including one held annually at Green Lake, as reported by James Teit. The Haida on the Queen Charlotte Islands obtained Rocky Mountain maple wood and cottonwood from the Mainland Tsimshian-speaking peoples, along with eulachon grease and other animal products. The Tsimshian in turn acquired large red cedar bark sheets for roofing from the Haida.

The trading of finished products was equally common and widespread. The Lower Lillooet, for example, sold split cedar-root baskets and birch-bark baskets from the Interior to their Coastal neighbours. The Haida, renowned for their wood carving ability, sold kerfed cedar oil-boxes and large canoes to the Tsimshian, said to be not as skilled at making these items. Similarly, the Nootka sold their excellent canoes far and wide among their Salish neighbours to the south and even to the Chinook on the lower Columbia and the peoples along the central Oregon Coast. They and the Kwakiutl traded their famous yellow cedar-bark robes both north and south along the Coast. The Shuswap bought Indian hemp products, including bags, baskets, and mats, from the Okanagan, and sold to them such items as birch-bark baskets.

Not only were finished products exchanged among Indian groups, but so were the actual techniques and skills involved in making them. For example, the Bella Coola learned from the Carrier and Chilcotin how to make birch-bark baskets and canoes, although they never became as skilled as their teachers at the art. Some ethnologists suggest that the technique of making twined baskets was learned by the Coast Salish from the Kwakiutl and Nootka; originally the Salish on the Coast were thought to have made only coiled baskets like their Interior Salish relatives. Similarly, it is believed that the Kwakiutl and Nootka learned the art of making sewn mats of cat-tail and tule only recently from their Salish neighbours. In many cases it is impossible to determine where or with which group a particular skill or technique involving plant materials originated. Indeed, a more intimate knowledge of the development of various botanical technologies among the native peoples of our Province could tell us much about the origins and inter-relationships of the people themselves.

ALGAE

(Including seaweeds and fresh-water and terrestrial types)

One type of seaweed, bull kelp (*Nereocystis luetkeana*), was of major significance in Coastal Indian technology. It is described in detail. A number of others were used as materials in minor capacities. The floats of giant kelp (*Macrocystis integrifolia* Bory), sometimes called "Indian firecrackers," were dried by Nootka children and put in the fire to make them explode. Haida children liked to squirt water out of the sacs of *Halosaccion glandiforme*

Sea wrack (*Fucus gardneri*) with lobed receptacles and sac alga
(*Halosaccion glandiforme*).

—Robert D. Turner

(Gmelin) Ruprecht, pretending at least within the last century, that they were the nipples of a cow. They also stepped on plants of *Leathesia difformis* (L.) Areschoug and the swollen receptacles of sea wrack, or "rockweed", (*Fucus gardneri* Silva) to make them pop. Some Nootkan peoples, such as the Hesquiat, played a type of "Indian hockey" on the beach, using pucks of dried sections of the stems of brown algae including *Laminaria* species.

Most Coastal Indian groups used sea wrack and other seaweeds such as *Porphyra perforata* J. Agardh., piling them over hot rocks to generate steam for cooking, bending and molding wood, or medicinal sweatbaths. They were also used to cover fish in boats or canoes to keep them cool on hot days. The Squamish rubbed sea wrack plants on their fishing lines to remove the human scent. When gardens were established following contact with Europeans, sea-weeds such as boa kelp [*Egregia menziesii* (Turner) Areschoug] were used to fertilize potatoes and other vegetables in some areas.

Several Interior Indian groups, including the Thompson, Carrier, and Tahltan, obtained a green dye for basket materials by boiling rotten, decayed wood, presumably by extracting terrestrial green algae from the wood. The Thompson also used "green pond slime," from colonies of *Spirogyra* and other aquatic algae, as a green pigment.

Bull Kelp	*Nereocystis luetkeana* (**Mertens**) **Postels & Ruprecht**
(Brown Algae)	**(Phaeophyceae)**

BOTANTICAL DESCRIPTION—One of the largest marine algae. The stalk is slender, unbranched, up to 30 m (100 ft) long, and attached to the bottom by a stout, root-like holdfast. It is solid below, becoming hollow and increasing in diameter at the upper end. It terminates in a large, spherical float, up to 15 cm (6 in.) in diameter. Attached to the upper surface of the float are two clusters of flat, elongated, leaf-like blades, each 6–15 cm (2.4–6.0 in.) broad and up to 4.5 m (14 ft) long. The entire plant is golden brown to dark brown.

HABITAT—On rocky bottom in the upper subtidal zone and to a depth of several fathoms, often growing in thick beds of several acres in sheltered inlets and bays.

DISTRIBUTION IN BRITISH COLUMBIA—Along the entire Pacific Coast.

INDIAN USE—The long, rope-like stalks were dried and cured, then spliced or plaited together to make fishing lines, nets, ropes, and harpoon lines by virtually all Coastal Indian groups in the Province. Curing methods varied from alternately soaking in fresh water and drying by smoking over a fire, a procedure used by some Coast Salish groups, to drying and soaking in dogfish or whale oil, as practiced by the Nootka. Kelp lines were dried for storage, but had to be soaked in water before use, or they were extremely brittle. After soaking they were strong and flexible.

Bull kelp (*Nereocystis luetkeana*).

—Robert D. Turner

Haida fishermen formerly kept a number of kelp lines of different lengths—one 200 fathoms, two of 50 fathoms, and one or two of 10 fathoms. To catch deep-water fish, such as halibut, about 10 people would tie their longest lines together and fasten all the hooks toward the end. Kelp was also used to make anchor lines, and often fishermen would simply fasten their boats to living kelp plants firmly anchored on the bottom.

The hollow upper stalks and bulb-like floats were employed throughout the Coast as storage containers for eulachon grease, fish oil, water, and even the European product molasses. They were cured by soaking in fresh water, then dried. The liquid was poured into the float or into a length of stipe with one end tied, and the tube was sealed by tying the other end. The knot could be untied at any time to squeeze out a required amount of liquid, then retied for further storage. These tubular containers could be coiled and laid in wooden chests or hung in a convenient place. Some Nootkan groups used fresh kelp floats as molds for deer suet. They poured the melted fat in through the hollow

45

stem, allowed it to harden, then broke the kelp away, leaving a "bulb" of suet ready for storage.

Some Coast Salish groups used kelp to form the warp in baskets, mats and blankets, but its brittleness when dry made it generally unsuitable for this purpose. The Coast Salish and other groups made halibut hooks by placing Douglas-fir and hemlock knots inside hollow kelp stalks and burying them overnight in hot ashes to make them easy to mold. In a similar manner, the Straits Salish placed the ends of yew wood bows inside lengths of kelp and steamed them to mold and bend to the desired shape. Squamish fishermen used kelp blades to keep fish fresh and moist in the canoe. The Comox used them to line steam-cooking pits to flavour the food and help generate steam.

Haida fishing line of bull kelp (#2—15551, R. H. Lowie Museum of Anthropology, Berkeley).

—Dorothy I. D. Kennedy

The Kwakiutl used the hollow tubes in their steaming pits to add water to the hot rocks at the bottom during the cooking process. They also buried the stalks under the dance house floor to achieve special effects during winter dances, such as having voices coming from the middle of the fire. The Bella Coola used lengths of kelp as water conduits; their name for the modern garden hose means "kelp."

In addition to these uses, kelp was employed in various recreational activities. The Straits Salish and the Haida used the stalks as targets in throwing games. Coast Salish and Kwakiutl children used them as a source of ammunition for their toy elderberry stem blowguns. They hung the stalks around their necks and tore off small pieces as they needed them.

LICHENS (LICHENES)

One species of lichen, wolf lichen (*Letharia vulpina*), was widely used by British Columbia Indians as a pigment and is discussed in detail. Other lichens were also used as materials, but on a more restricted basis. The black tree lichens [*Alectoria fremontii* Tuck. and others in the *A. jubata* complex] and their close relative, the light green "old man's beard" lichen [*A. sarmentosa* (Ach.) Ach.] were sometimes used by the Lillooet and other Interior Salish peoples for weaving items of clothing, such as ponchos and footwear. However, they were not considered a high quality material, and were usually used only by poorer people who could not obtain skins for clothing. The were usually interwoven with some stronger fibrous material such as silverberry bark. These species were also used by some groups, including the Shuswap and Bella Coola, as false whiskers and artificial hair for decorating dance masks and masquerading, especially by children. The Sechelt used "old man's beard" for baby diapers, and put it on the fire when smoke was desired. The Haida used it and a similar lichen (*Usnea longissima* Ach.) to strain hot pitch to remove impurities before it was used as a medicine. According to one source, some Coast Salish used a species of *Usnea* to make a dark green dye, and "*Alectoria jubata*" with *Letharia vulpina* to make a yellow dye, but this use has not been substantiated by modern informants.

Black tree lichen (*Alectoria fremontii*) on western larch (*Larix occidentalis*).
—Nancy J. Turner

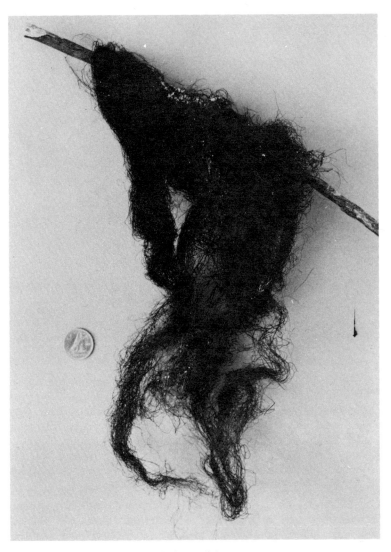

Black tree lichen.

—Robert D. Turner

Shoes made of black tree lichen by Thompson Indians (#85710, Field Museum of Natural History, Chicago).

—Dorothy I. D. Kennedy

Wolf Lichen — *Letharia vulpina* Wain.

OTHER NAME—Wolf "moss."

BOTANICAL DESCRIPTION—A short, upright, densely branching, bright yellowish-green lichen 2.5–5 cm (1–2 in.) tall, which grows on coniferous trees and wood. The individual branches are wiry and round in cross-section, bearing greenish powdery fragments called soredia. The fruiting disks, when present, are small (about 5 mm across), brown and flat. This species contains a brightly coloured but poisonous lichen acid known as vulpinic acid, which is responsible for the striking colouring of the thallus.

HABITAT—Grows on branches, dead wood, and bark of coniferous trees such as Douglas-fir (*Pseudotsuga menziesii*), ponderosa pine (*Pinus ponderosa*), and western larch (*Larix occidentalis*). Commonly grows with the long, hair-like black tree lichen (*Alectoria fremontii*).

50

Wolf lichen (*Letharia vulpina*) on a dead branch of ponderosa pine
(*Pinus ponderosa*).

—Robert D. Turner

DISTRIBUTION IN BRITISH COLUMBIA—Throughout the Interior, especially in montane forests and the dry areas of the south. It also occurs sporadically west of the Cascades, where it is generally stunted and less dense.

INDIAN USE—Lichens are well known in many areas of the world as sources of dyes. Many lichen acids are either themselves brightly coloured or yield pigments on reaction with chemical substances. Among British Columbia Indians the only lichen used to any extent for dyeing was the wolf lichen, which yields a brilliant yellow dye. It was used by virtually all the Interior groups, including Kootenay, Salishan, and Athapaskan, as well as the Flathead Salish of Montana and the Blackfoot of Alberta. It was used by some Coastal groups as well, when available. The Tlingit of Alaska, for example, obtained it by trade from the Interior to colour their spruce-root baskets.

The simplest way to extract the pigment is to boil the lichen in water, then steep the item to be coloured in the solution. The Okanagan sometimes added Oregon grape bark to the water to intensify the colour. Basket materials, fur, moccasins, feathers, porcupine quills, wood, and in modern times, cloth, were all coloured with this pigment. The Thompson, and perhaps some other groups, used it as a face and body paint. They simply dipped the lichen in water and brushed it on the skin, or wet the skin and applied it dry.

FUNGI

Tree fungi, especially the Indian paint fungus (*Echinodontium tinctorium*) were widely utilized in Indian technology, while mushrooms and fleshy fungi played a very minor role. According to one informant, the Thompson people used the inky cap (*Coprinus micaceus* Fr.) with water sprinkled on it for killing flies and other insects. Blackfoot men of Alberta formerly wore necklaces of golf-ball-sized puffballs (*Lycoperdon* sp.), said to be prized for their delicate odour. These puffballs also inspired the designs on some Blackfoot teepees. The uses of the various tree fungi are described in more detail in the following sections.

Indian Paint Fungus   *Echinodontium tinctorium*
                                          Ell. & Everh.

(Polypore Family)   **(Polyporaceae)**

BOTANICAL DESCRIPTION—A close relative of the bracket fungi, growing mainly on coniferous trees. The fruiting structures are woody and rounded, averaging about 5 cm (2 in.) across. The spores are produced in crowded circular pores on the undersurface. The external and internal tissue is bright red-orange.

HABITAT—Found mainly on the trunks of living coniferous trees, such as hemlock (*Tsuga heterophylla*), Douglas-fir (*Pseudotsuga menziesii*), and true firs (*Abies* spp.).

DISTRIBUTION IN BRITISH COLUMBIA—Occurs throughout the Province, but is locally abundant in certain areas, such as in the Coastal Western Hemlock zone.

Indian paint fungus (*Echinodontium tinctorium*) collected in Squamish territory (#VIIG 254, National Museum of Man, Ottawa).

—Dorothy I. D. Kennedy

INDIAN USE—This fungus was used as a red pigment in many areas of the Province, although in most cases its identity was established only from informants' descriptions. Records of its use extend to the following groups: Okanagan, Thompson, Lower Lillooet, Straits Salish, Sechelt, Kwakiutl, Nootka, Haida, Tsimshian and Tahltan. Undoubtedly other groups used it as well. The Haida reportedly obtained it by trade from the Tsimshian on the Mainland. The main use of the pigment was as a face paint, for cosmetic purposes, and to protect the skin from sunburn or insect bites. The Tahltan used it to absorb some of the sun's glare on the snow, reducing the chances of snow blindness. The standard method of preparation of the paint was to dry the fungus, usually by heating it in a fire, then powder it and mix it with melted fat, grease, or pitch. The resulting salve was smeared directly on the face. The Tahltan simply applied a thin layer of suet to the skin, then powdered the fungus over the top. The Saanich mixed red cedar bark and red alder bark with the fungus before heating it and used the powder for tattooing. The Kwakiutl mixed it with hemlock gum as a face paint, but also made a general purpose paint by placing the fungus on hot stones, covering it with wet lady fern [*Athyrium filix-femina* (L.) Roth.] and leaving it until it became a red powder. Like most natural dyes and pigments the paint fungus is seldom used today.

Bracket Fungi	*Fomes* species, *Ganoderma* species, and *Polyporus* species
(Polypore Family)	**(Polyporaceae)**

OTHER NAMES—Shelf fungi, polypores.

BOTANICAL DESCRIPTION—These fungi are found on living or dead tree trunks, as well as on stumps and fallen timber. The vegetative portion, the mycelium, penetrates deeply into the wood, softening it and ultimately causing it to rot and crumble. It can often be seen as a white or yellow cottony substance beneath the bark or in the cracks of rotting wood. The fruiting portion is more conspicuous, consisting of woody or leathery, flattened to hoof-shaped, "brackets." The upper surface is hard, varying from light brown to orange-brown to greyish, depending on the species. The lower surface is usually white, with innumerable closely packed, rounded pores in which the spores are produced. Many species are perennial, the size of the fruiting structures increasing by annual additions to the pore surface and outer edge. Some attain a size of 3 dm (1 ft) or more across. They can usually be removed from the tree or log by applying pressure to the upper surface.

HABITAT—Bracket fungi grow on living and dead wood of both coniferous and deciduous trees. Many types show a preference for coniferous or deciduous hosts, and some for individual species of trees.

DISTRIBUTION IN BRITISH COLUMBIA—The above genera and their relatives are widely distributed in the Province, especially in moist woods.

INDIAN USE—In ethnographic literature and amongst contemporary native informants the different species of bracket fungi are

Bracket fungus [*Fomes pinicola* (Swartz) Cooke].

—Nancy J. Turner

seldom distinguished, other than by specifying their host tree. The corky inner tissue of some species was used by a number of groups as punk for "slow matches." When ignited it smoulders for many hours. A flame can be obtained for kindling a fire simply by blowing on it. The Kwakiutl used a fungus growing on grand fir, while the Lower Lillooet used a soft fungus, "as yellow as sulphur," probably the sulphur polypore [*Polyporus sulphureus* (Bull.) Fr.], which is edible when young. Another species used by British Columbia Indians, the tinderwood polypore (*Fomes*

55

fomentarius Gill.), has been employed commercially in manufacturing German tinder or "punk sticks" for lighting cigars and pipes on windy days and touching off fireworks. For this purpose it was ground into small pieces, then glued onto sticks and dipped in saltpetre. Native people used clam shells, cedar bark or birch bark to contain the fungus punk for transport. The Blackfoot of Alberta carried it in a covered buffalo horn lined with moist, rotten wood.

The Thompson reportedly did not use fungus as tinder, although they had heard of foreigners using it. However, they did use a type of fungus from cottonwood trees, possibly *Ganoderma applanatum* (Pers.) Pat., to tan buckskin. If the cottonwood fungus was not available, any type of bracket fungus could be used. It was chopped and mixed with deer brain and water. The hide was stripped of hair and allowed to soak in this mixture for a few hours. Then a small amount of fish oil or, in modern times, butter, was added and the skin was left to soak for four days. It was then taken out, laced to a frame, and worked with the hands, first on one face and then the other, until it was dry. The entire process was then repeated, following which, the hide was smudged over a fire made with bracket fungus and rotten wood and covered with earth to prevent the hide from burning. When it had been smoked on both sides, the hide was again soaked in the fungus-deer-brain-water mixture, and again stretched and worked with the hands. By this time it was soft and white, suitable for use in making clothing or bags, although a perfectionist might subject it to the entire process of smoking, soaking, and stretching one final time before using it. The Sechelt tanned hides by burying them for several weeks with a small, scallop-like polypore (*Polyporus versicolor* L. ex Fr.). Other groups may have also used bracket fungi for tanning.

The Haida used the cottony mycelium of a fungus growing on rotten Sitka spruce, rubbed into a soft paste, as caulking for canoes and oil boxes. The Squamish used the corky inner tissue of *Fomes* and *Polyporus* brackets for scrubbing the hands. The Bella Coola painted faces on large specimens of bracket fungi, attached miniature bodies of cedar bark to them, and used them as dance symbols

Sulphur polypore (*Polyporus sulphureus*).

—Nancy J. Turner

in a special "fungus dance" of the Kusiut ceremonials. The Stalo
and certain Washington Salish groups used a lump of fungus as a
target in a bow and arrow game, and the Kwakiutl used a round
one in a handball game. There was a widespread belief amongst
Coast Salish peoples that tree fungi caused echoes in the woods.

MOSSES (BRYOPHYTA)

With the exception of the distinctive and extremely useful
sphagnum mosses, which are discussed in detail, most ethnographic
sources and native people do not distinguish between the many
different species of mosses and liverworts. Mosses were used
throughout the Province for numerous general household tasks,
such as lining steaming pits and generating steam for cooking and
molding wood, wiping the slime off fish, covering floors, stuffing
mattresses and pillows, lining baby bags and cradles, and, mixed
with pitch, for caulking canoes. Within the last two centuries they
were mixed with mud and used to chink log cabins. Groups having
easy access to sphagnum moss usually preferred it for these jobs,
but if it were not available, any kind of moss was used, with
preference given to bulky, absorbant types. Diamond Jenness
reports that the Saanich Indians used *Leucolepis menziesii*
(Hook.) Steere to make a yellow dye for basket materials, and
G. T. Emmons records that the Tahltan used *Hypnum capillifolium*
Wornstorf. to line the cradle of a newborn baby, although James
Teit states that they used sphagnum for this purpose. The Flathead
Salish of Montana used *Claopodium crispifolium* (Hook.) Ren. &
Card. for lining cradle boards and padding inside baby diapers.
It was said to last a full 12 hours without needing changing.

Sphagnum Moss	*Sphagnum* **species**
(Sphagnum Family)	**(Sphagnaceae)**

OTHER NAMES—"Indian sponge," "baby moss," "diaper moss,"
peat moss, bog moss.

BOTANICAL DESCRIPTION—These are large, attractive mosses
of acid bogs and muskegs. Their long, weak stems are crowded

together, forming soft cushions and extensive beds often covering several acres. Alternate clusters of branches are borne along the stem and at the top is a dense rosette of branches. The plants vary in colour from whitish to golden to yellow-green, depending on the species and on environmental conditions. The leaves are

Sphagnum moss (*Sphagnum capillaceum*).

—Nancy J. Turner

small, veinless, and only one cell-layer thick, but with a unique structure readily visible under a low-power microscope. They consist of two kinds of cells, one large, colourless, and hollow, with pores on the surfaces which allow air and water to pass through readily, and the second small and elongated, containing active cell contents and chlorophyll and forming a network around the large empty cells. It is the large cells which give sphagnum mosses their incredible absorbent properties, enabling them to take up and hold water like a sponge. The spore cases are dark brown and globular, on thick, stocky pedicels. There are many species of *Sphagnum* in the Province. *Sphagnum capillaceum* (Weiss) Schrank, *S. palustre* L., and *S. squarrosum* Crome, are among the most common.

HABITAT—Shaded to open swampy or boggy sites in acid soil from sea level to subalpine elevations.

DISTRIBUTION IN BRITISH COLUMBIA—In appropriate habitats throughout the Province.

INDIAN USE—The soft, absorbent qualities of sphagnum moss made it ideal for use in personal hygiene and baby care. It was preferred over other types of mosses for bedding, sanitary napkins, wound dressings, and baby diapers. It was especially used by the northern groups, such as the Tahltan, having access to large muskeg areas where sphagnum is a dominant ground cover. Tahltan women, about to be confined for childbearing, gathered and stored large quantities of sphagnum. It was used to carpet the lodge in which the baby was to be born, to wipe the new-born baby's skin, and to line its bark cradle. As the baby grew, the moss was placed between its legs as a diaper and held by a soft breech clout of marmot or other skin. This diaper would last for many hours without being changed. If necessary, it could be washed, dried, and re-used. The Carrier used only the light-coloured sphagnums for diapers; the red ones were said to cause bad sores.

FERNS AND FERN-ALLIES (PTERIDOPHYTA)

Hosetails, sword-fern, and bracken fern, were widely used in British Columbia Indian technology, and are discussed in detail in this section. Several other ferns and fern-allies were utilized on a more limited basis. Running clubmoss (*Lycopodium clavatum* L.) was used in modern times by the Bella Coola and Nootka to make wreaths and Christmas decorations, although a Thompson informant stated that it would bring bad luck if kept in the house. The Thompson, as well as the Tlingit of Alaska and the Makah and Quinault of Washington, used the shiny black stems of the maidenhair fern (*Adiantum pedatum* L.) to imbricate baskets. George Dawson records that the Shuswap used lady fern (*Athyrium filix-femina* (L.) Roth.) to make a black dye, although he gives no details as to how it was prepared. The Kwakiutl placed lady fern fronds over Indian paint fungus when heating it to make a red paint. The Kwakiutl and Coast Salish used the thin, wiry roots of the spiny wood fern (*Dryopteris austriaca* (Jacq.) Woynar ex Schinz & Thell.) as tinder for making a "slow match" (*see also* bracket fungi). A bundle of roots was enclosed within a mussel or clam shell and ignited. The shell could then be buried or carried on trips and the fern roots would smoulder for several days. The fronds of the Oregon woodsia (*Woodsia oregana* D. C. Eaton) and other ferns were used by the Shuswap for covering and pressing down the berries in a basket to prevent them from spilling. In Okanagan country, the presence of ferns of any type was considered to be an indication of water for hunters and travellers.

Horsetails   *Equisetum* species

(Horsetail Family)   **(Equisetaceae)**

OTHER NAMES—Scouring rush, "Indian sandpaper."

BOTANICAL DESCRIPTION—These are herbaceous perennials with deep, spreading, dark-coloured rhizomes and conspicuously jointed stems. Depending on the species, the stems are either all alike, or of two kinds, one fertile and lacking chlorophyll, and therefore whitish in colour, and the other vegetative. They are usually erect, simple or branching, hollow, except at the nodes or "joints," and cylindrical, with many regular longitudinal grooves. The cell walls of the epidermis are impregnated with silicon and often there are well-developed silicified ridges between the grooves, making the plants rough and "scratchy" to the touch. The leaves are very small and scale-like, growing in whorls at each node and fused at the base to form a notched sheath, usually with dark markings. When branches are present they are in whorls, borne at the nodes. The sporangia are borne in terminal cones, on separate fertile shoots or at the tips of the vegetative growth. Several species were used by British Columbia Indians, including the common horsetail (*E. arvense* L.) and the giant horsetail (*E. telmateia* Ehrh.), both branching species with separate fertile and vegetative shoots, the former up to 7.5 dm (2.5 ft) tall, the latter up to 2 m (6.6 ft) tall, and the common scouring rush (*E. hiemale* L.), a non-branching species up to 1.5 m (about 5 ft) tall with stems all of one type.

Giant horsetail (*Equisetum telmateia*).

—Robert D. Turner

Common scouring rush (*Equisetum hiemale*).

—Nancy J. Turner

HABITAT—*E. telmateia* and *E. hiemale* grow in low, wet ground, in swamps and along streams and seepage areas, while *E. arvense* grows in a wide variety of habitats, often along roadsides or in wasteland areas.

DISTRIBUTION IN BRITISH COLUMBIA—*E. telmateia* is widely distributed along the Coast as far north as the Queen Charlotte Islands but does not occur in the Interior; *E. hiemale* and *E. arvense* are widespread throughout the Province.

INDIAN USE—The rough, silicon-impregnated cell walls of the horsetails make them ideal for smoothing and polishing surfaces. Most native people today equate them with sandpaper. The Coastal peoples and some Interior groups used them for polishing wooden objects, such as canoes, feast dishes, arrow shafts, gambling sticks, and, within the last century, knitting needles, although in some areas dogfish skin was preferred for these purposes. The Coastal groups used all three species, but especially *E. telmateia,* while the Interior peoples used *E. arvense* and *E. hiemale,* not having access to *E. telmateia.*

The Thompson, Okanagan, and Shuswap peoples used horsetails for polishing and sharpening bone tools and for smoothing and finishing soapstone pipes. For the latter, the Thompson sometimes used a mixture of grease and lodgepole pine pitch along with the horsetails. The Okanagan coated their pipes with salmon slime, allowed it to harden, then rubbed the surface with the horsetails. The Okanagan used them to polish their fingernails. The Lillooet used them to sharpen arrowheads.

In addition to their use as abrasives, horsetails were used by some groups in the decorative imbrication of baskets. The black underground rhizomes were the part employed for this purpose. The Tlingit of Alaska used marsh horsetail rhizomes (*E. palustre* L.), and probably those of other species, to imbricate their fine spruce-root baskets. The Coast Salish peoples of British Columbia and Washington used the rhizomes and stems of *E. telmateia* for their baskets, and the Sanpoil-Nespelem, a Washington Okanagan group, used *E. hiemale* rhizomes to imbricate both baskets and storage bags. The Blackfoot of Alberta crushed the stems to make a light pink dye for colouring porcupine quills.

Sword-fern

(Fern Family)

Polystichum munitum
(Kaulf.) Presl.

(Polypodiaceae)

BOTANICAL DESCRIPTION—A perennial with stout, fleshy rhizomes. The fronds are coarse and erect, often 60 cm (24 in.) or more in length, and growing in clumps. The young fronds are light green, becoming dark green with age, and remaining green over the winter. The stems are greenish and scaly. The pinnae are numerous, alternate, toothed, and attached to the stem at a single point. Each has a prominent projection or "hilt" at the base of the upper edge. The sori are numerous, usually occurring in two rows on the undersurface of the upper pinnae, with indusia. The general shape of the frond is long, flat, and tapering to a point at the top.

HABITAT—Common in damp, rich woods and on shaded slopes, but also occurs as a smaller form on open, rocky exposures. Generally confined to lowland forests.

Sword-fern (*Polystichum munitum*).

—Robert D. Turner

Widespread and extremely common west of the Coastal mountains. A dominant fern in lowland Coastal forests rich in humus.

Indian use—The long, stiff fronds were gathered in quantity and used by most Coastal groups, and some Interior groups such as Lillooet and Thompson within the range of the species, to line steaming pits, storage boxes, baskets, and berry drying racks, and to lay fish on and wipe them, to cover the floors of summer houses and dance houses, and to sleep on. For the last, they were sometimes woven into crude mats. Squamish children and those of other southern Coastal groups played an endurance game with the fronds to see who could pull off the most pinnae, saying "pála" with each one, in a single breath. The Squamish sometimes call this fern "pála-pála." The Thompson often copied the sword-fern pattern in the designs on their split cedar-root baskets.

Bracken Fern	*Pteridium aquilinum* (L.) Kuhn.
(Fern Family)	**(Polypodiaceae)**

Other name—Brake fern.

Botanical description—This is the largest, most common fern in British Columbia, often exceeding 15 dm (5 ft). The thick, fleshy rhizomes are perennial, often 20 cm (8 in.) deep, running horizontally for long distances, frequently branching. They are black outside, with a white inner tissue and tough longitudinal fibres in the centre. The fronds are borne individually along the rhizomes, having tall, smooth, light green stems and coarsely branching pinnae. The fronds and lower pinnae are broadly triangular in shape. The pinnules are numerous and deeply toothed, and the sori, when present, are marginal.

Habitat—Grows in a variety of habitats, commonly in open forests and clearings at low and moderate elevations.

Distribution in British Columbia—Found generally throughout the Province, except at high elevations.

Bracken fern (*Pteridium aquilinum*).

—Robert D. Turner

INDIAN USE—The large fronds, like those of the sword-fern, were used for many household purposes, including lining steam cooking pits, particularly by the Okanagan, covering berry baskets, storing dried foods on, wiping fish, and as bedding. In the old days, the Kootenay made sunshades from them. Within the last century, the Bella Coola used the dead fronds to mulch their potato hills. The Nootka and Kwakiutl saved the fibrous remnants from the edible rhizomes, dried them, and used them for tinder and punk for "slow matches." Contained in clam shells or tightly bound in cedar bark, they would hold a fire for many hours. According to the notes of Diamond Jenness, the Straits Salish and Halkomelem used bundles of the fibres of bracken fern rhizomes for torches in February; at other times of the year they used bundled cedar sticks. The Haida used the fronds as a design for basket patterns.

CONIFERS AND THEIR RELATIVES
(GYMNOSPERMAE)

Yellow Cedar *Chamaecyparis nootkatensis* **(Lamb.) Spach**

(Cypress Family) **(Cupressaceae)**

OTHER NAMES—Yellow cypress, Alaska cedar or cypress, Sitka cedar or cypress, Nootka cedar or cypress.

BOTANICAL DESCRIPTION—A large tree, 20–40 m (65–135 ft) or more high and 1 m (3 ft) or more in diameter, although gnarled and stunted individuals occur in unfavourable habitats. The bark is thin and greyish-brown, tending to shed in long, narrow, shaggy strips. The wood is yellow and pungent smelling. The branches are horizontal, well-spaced, and drooping, and the branchlets, covered with small, scale-like, bluish-green leaves, are flat, hanging, and prickly to the touch. The cones are spherical, about 1.2 cm (0.5 in.) across, with up to six thickened, woody scales. The seeds are about 3 mm (0.1 in.) long, golden-brown, and winged. The over-all appearance of the tree is very similar to that of red cedar, but more drooping and shaggy.

Yellow cedar (*Chamaecyparis nootkatensis*).

—Nancy J. Turner

HABITAT—Damp Coastal forests, usually at subalpine elevations. Also occurs in peat bogs and muskegs, and in rock crevices, where it is usually stunted.

DISTRIBUTION IN BRITISH COLUMBIA—A common species of Coastal subalpine forests from Vancouver Island to Alaska, mostly west of the Cascade and Coast Mountains between 650 and 2 300 m (2,000 and 7,000 ft), but extending to near sea level in the north, and reported from Slocan Lake in the Kootenays.

INDIAN USE—The tough, straight-grained wood was used for carving implements by virtually all Coastal Indian peoples. Yellow cedar bows were very popular and were common trading items. The Fraser River Lillooet obtained them, or the wood to make them, from the Lower Lillooet of the Pemberton area. The Saanich traded them from Mainland Salish groups. The Sechelt used only wood from young trees for bows. In addition, the Vancouver Island Salish used yellow cedar wood for carving paddles and, in modern times, knitting needles. The Nootka carved masks

Yellow cedar bark drying, Masset (Haida).

—Robert D. Turner

from it. The Kwakiutl used it for paddles, chests, dishes, and fishing net hoops, and the Haida for digging sticks, adze handles, paddles, dishes and, recently, bedposts.

The inner bark has the same fibrous qualities as red cedar bark, but is considered even more valuable because it is finer and softer, and lighter in colour when dry. It was pulled off the trees in long strands and split and dried much like red cedar bark. The Kwakiutl soaked it for 12 days in warm salt water in a quiet bay at the low water line, then pounded it on a flat stone with a whalebone beater to make it soft and piable, dried it for four days, and stored it. For further details of preparation, *see* red cedar (*Thuja plicata*). The prepared bark was used throughout the Coast especially for weaving clothing and blankets, where it was preferred to red cedar bark because of its softness. Often it was interwoven with duck down or mountain goat wool, or was trimmed with these substances. It was also used to weave mats and hats, and for decorating masks. Shredded, it served as bandaging and for washing babies.

Rocky Mountain Juniper

Juniperus scopulorum
Sarg.

(Cypress Family)

(Cupressaceae)

OTHER NAMES—Rocky Mountain red cedar, red cedar.

BOTANICAL DESCRIPTION—A densely branching tree up to 10 m (30 ft) high, also found as a sprawling shrub less than 1 m (3 ft) high. The bark is stringy and reddish-brown and the leaves are small, bluish-green, and mostly scale-like, the juvenile ones needle-like. Male and female cones are produced on separate trees. The ovulate cones are round and berry-like, bluish-purple with a whitish waxy coating, 5–6 mm (0.20–0.23 in.) across, mostly 1 or 2 seeded, maturing in two seasons. The foliage and fruit have a sharp pungent odour, especially when crushed.

HABITAT—Rocky Coastal islands, dry plains and valleys, and lower mountains.

Rocky Mountain juniper (*Juniperus scopulorum*).

—Robert D. Turner

DISTRIBUTION IN BRITISH COLUMBIA—Dry sites from Coastal Vancouver Island and the Gulf Islands eastward to the Rocky Mountains and north to the Peace and Stikine Rivers.

INDIAN USE—The wood is extremely tough and was considered by the Interior Salish peoples—the Lillooet, Thompson, Okanagan, and Shuswap—as well as by the Carrier, to be one of the best materials for making bows. Additionally, the Thompson used it to make hoops and clubs and for hafting implements, and the Okanagan used it to make a type of spoked wheel used in a throwing game and, after horses were introduced, to make double-trees. The Shuswap used it to make snowshoe frames and spears. The Carrier and perhaps some other groups made rough temporary spoons from the inner bark, and the Thompson made elongated juniper bark baskets.

The pungent boughs were used by virtually every group within the range of the tree, from the Straits Salish of Vancouver Island to

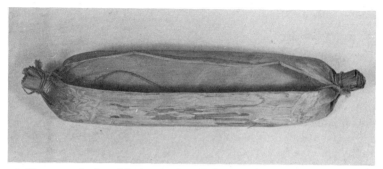

A Thompson basket of juniper bark (#II C243, National Museum of Man, Ottawa).

—Dorothy I. D. Kennedy

the Blackfoot of Alberta and the Flathead of Montana, as an "incense" to clean and fumigate houses and purify the air, especially following an illness or death. It is said to protect the inhabitants from bad spirits. The branches were burned in the fire or placed on top of the stove and allowed to smoke, or simply hung around the walls, or boiled in water to make a washing solution for floors, walls, bed-clothes, and furniture. The Flathead used the boughs as a body scent. The Kootenay used bundles of them to sprinkle water on the hot rocks during sweat bathing. The Thompson used the wood as a fuel for smoking hides, often combining it with big sagebrush when a dark skin was desired. The Shuswap noted that juniper wood should not be used for cooking because it will impart a bitter flavour to the food. The Thompson used a strong decoction of the berry-like cones to kill ticks on horses, and the Okanagan soaked their arrows overnight in a solution of pounded juniper branches to make a deer's blood coagulate quickly when it was hit, preventing it from running very far. Interestingly, one medicinal use of juniper by the Okanagan is as an emergency blood coagulant, to stop internal hemorrhaging. The Blackfoot, and probably some British Columbia groups as well, used the "berries" as beads, often interspersed with silverberry fruits.

73

Western Red Cedar   *Thuja plicata* Donn
(Cypress Family)   (Cupressaceae)

OTHER NAMES—Giant arborvitae, Pacific red cedar, giant cedar.

BOTANICAL DESCRIPTION—A large tree up to 70 m (230 ft) high and 4.3 m (14 ft) across; mature individuals are often fluted and strongly buttressed at the base. The bark is thin, greyish outside and reddish-brown inside, longitudinally ridged and fissured, readily pulling off in long fibrous strips. The wood is light, aromatic, straight-grained, and rot-resistant. The branches tend to spread outward and the branchlets are flat, spray-like, hanging, and yellowish-green, usually turning brown and shedding after about 3 or 4 years. Unlike yellow cedar branchlets, they are not prickly to touch. The leaves are small, flattened, and scale-like. The pollen cones, borne at the branchlet tips, are numerous, reddish, and minute (about 2 mm long). The ovulate cones, green when immature, brown at maturity, are few-scaled, about 1 cm (0.4 in.) long, and oval shaped, borne in loose clusters on the surface of the branchlets. The scales spread open when dry to release the seeds, which are laterally winged.

HABITAT—Rich, moist to swampy soils, usually in shaded forests.

DISTRIBUTION IN BRITISH COLUMBIA—A dominant tree in moist forest habitats along the Coast from Vancouver Island to Alaska; also occurs on moist slopes and in valleys of the Interior, north to 50°30′ latitude, and up to about 1 400 m (4,500 ft) elevation.

INDIAN USE—Of all the plants used as materials by British Columbia Indians, red cedar was without doubt the most widely employed and the most versatile. The strong, light wood is both easily worked and rot-resistant. It was used by all Coastal groups and, to a lesser extent, by Interior groups within the range of the tree. On the Coast it was used to the exclusion of almost all other species to make dugout canoes, house posts and planks, totem poles and mortuary posts, and storage and cooking boxes. It was also

Western red cedar (*Thuja plicata*).

—Robert D. Turner

used for dishes, arrow shafts, harpoon shafts, spear poles, barbecuing sticks, fish spreaders and hangers, dipnet hooks, fish clubs, masks, rattles, benches, cradles, coffins, herring rakes, canoe bailers, ceremonial drums, combs, fishing floats, berry drying racks and frames, fish weirs, spirit whistles, and paddles. In the Interior, it was used in some areas, such as the Okanagan, for dugout canoes, and by Interior Salish peoples generally for various types of shelters, both temporary and permanent, as well as drying racks, spear shafts, dipnet frames, river poles, salmon spreaders, paddles, drum hoops, birch-bark canoe frames, bows, and arrows. Everywhere it was considered an excellent fuel, although fast burning. It is said to make a good fire for drying fish because it burns with little smoke. According to one Shuswap woman it is also good for curing and smoking hides because of its low pitch content. It was used by the

Koskimo fire maker using drill of red cedar wood. Photo by E. S. Curtis (*ca* 1914), courtesy Provincial Archives of British Columbia, Victoria.

76

Kwakiutl and other groups to make a drill and hearth for starting friction fires. Since contact with the White man, cedar wood was used by Indian peoples, as by Whites, for shingles and shakes, house siding, and fence posts.

In the days before European contact cedar trees were seldom felled. Instead, fallen logs or boards split from standing trees were used. Trees which were felled were laboriously cut around the base with adzes and chisels, or were sometimes burned at the bottom until they toppled. The Bella Coola bound a Rocky Mountain maple branch around the trunk and ignited it. It would smolder for many hours, gradually burning through the softer cedar wood until the tree fell.

Splitting off cedar boards, house planks and half-logs for canoes was accomplished by hammering in a series of graduated yew-wood or antler wedges along the grain. Carving the wood was done with adzes, chisels, knives, and drills. Even before European contact, some iron was available to Coastal peoples, but most tools were of stone, shell, bone, or horn. Nowhere else in North America was woodworking developed to such a fine art as with red cedar on the Pacific Coast, particularly on the central and northern Coast of British Columbia. Symmetry of form, neatness, and precision characterized the most utilitarian of cedar-wood objects. Paintings and relief carvings of stylized designs, usually of animal motifs, adorned many of them, and even undecorated items were carved with even rows of adze marks to produce aesthetically pleasing effects or were polished until they shone. The excellence and craftsmanship of native carvers of cedar is demonstrated not only by the well-known masks and totem poles which are famous the world over, but also, and perhaps to an even greater extent, by their dugout canoes and kerfed boxes.

The canoes were carved on the exterior surface first, and plugs were inserted into the hull to a depth equalling its desired thickness. Then the inside was hollowed out, usually by combined carving and controlled burning, down to the point where the pegs became visible. At this stage the canoe would be dragged out of the woods to the beach, or to a place more convenient for the carver to

Mrs. Florence Davidson of Masset, Queen Charlotte Islands (Haida), starting to pull off a strip of red cedar bark.

—Robert D. Turner

work. It was filled with water, which was heated to the boiling point with red-hot rocks. As the wood became softer and more flexible, it was spread at the top, so that the canoe was wider across than the original tree trunk. Cross-braces were inserted, fixed with wooden pegs, and on more elaborate types, separate prow and stern pieces were added to make the craft more seaworthy. The finished hull was polished with dogfish skin or horsetail and decorated. Canoes ranged in size from those built for one or two people to those used on trading or war expeditions, some of which could accommodate 60 men. These large craft were built mainly during the 18th and 19th centuries, when iron tools were plentiful.

The kerfed cedar boxes, made by groups of the central and northern Coast, including Nootka, Kwakiutl, Bella Coola, Haida, Tsimshian, and Tlingit, were a superb combination of artistry and utility. Many different sizes and shapes were made, all by the same basic technique. A wide, thin board was split from a cedar log, and three transverse grooves or kerfs were cut, spaced at intervals varying with the box's ultimate dimensions. The board was then steamed over a fire covered with wet moss or seaweed and the wood was allowed to soften. It was then "folded" along the kerfs to make a square or rectangular box. The fourth seam, where the ends joined together, was pegged together or "sewn" with spruce or cedar root. A flanged bottom board was fixed on with pegs and sewn so tightly that the box was watertight. Finally the box was fitted with a lid. Folded boxes were used for boiling or steaming food or for storing berries, fish, oil, or other products. More elaborate boxes, for higher class people or for storing ceremonial objects, were beautifully carved and decorated. Some types of folded boxes were used for cradles, others for coffins, and still others for feast dishes. Those used for storage in ocean-going canoes had angled kerfs so that when constructed they were wider at the top than at the base. In the past cedar boxes were widely traded along the coast and even into the Interior. Many people still own them today. The art of making them, once virtually forgotten, is slowly being revived by a few modern native craftsmen.

Strip of red cedar bark being pulled from tree.

—Robert D. Turner

Mrs. Florence Davidson breaking off the brittle outer bark of a strip of red cedar bark; note the bundles of cleaned bark ready to be carried home.

—Robert D. Turner

The slender, pliable branches, or withes, of red cedar were used as rope by many Coastal Indian peoples. They were usually gathered in the spring and were peeled and split in halves or quarters, or, if thin, were used whole. They were twisted and worked until soft and pliable, then used singly or plaited together for sewing wood, binding implements, tying boards onto house frames, or for anchor lines, harpoon lines, tree-climbing "belts," fishing lines, fish nets, and duck nets. Some of the anchor ropes of plaited cedar withe used by the Vancouver Island Salish were reportedly as thick as a man's wrist. A number of groups, including Nootka, Kwakiutl, Comox, Bella Coola, and Lower Lillooet made baskets of cedar withes, particularly open-weave baskets, and the Niska employed cedar withes to make fish traps. The Squamish used them for tying bundles of dried salmon. Some Coast Salish groups, such as the Nanaimo and Saanich of Vancouver Island, used bundles of dried cedar twigs as torches.

Cedar boughs were used as bedding in some areas, such as among the Shuswap and Squamish. The Saanich, Comox, and other Coastal groups sunk them in the ocean near the shore to catch herring spawn. The Comox threaded eulachons and herring onto the green boughs for drying and the Kwakiutl interspersed them with layers of edible seaweed being dried. The Thompson reportedly used them to make a green dye.

Cedar roots were used by groups, such as the Nootka and Kwakiutl, for lashings and for making nets, baskets, hats, and mats, but the Salish people, especially those of the Interior, who seemed to make little use of cedar withes, were by far the greatest users of the roots. The coiled split cedar-root baskets of the Interior Salish, particularly the Lillooet and Thompson, are world famous. The foundation coils of these baskets were made of inner cedar bark, cedar-root bark, or bundles of split cedar root, and were completely covered and, at the same time, stitched tightly together by split cedar-root strands. So closely were they sewn that the baskets were watertight, serving equally well as berry containers, water carriers, or cooking vessels. They were beautifully decorated by a process known as imbrication, in which strips of material such as bitter cherry bark and ryegrass are superimposed over the

A red cedar bark gatherer; note the adze in the woman's hand, the bundles of bark on her back, and her clothing made of red cedar bark. Photo by E. S. Curtis (*ca.* 1915), courtesy Provincial Archives of British Columbia.

A Bella Coola ceremonial neck ring of red cedar bark (#2322, Ethnology Division, British Columbia Provincial Museum, Victoria).

—Robert D. Turner

basic cedar root to produce geometric designs and patterns of plant and animal motifs. They varied considerably in size and shape, the most common style being rectangular with a small, flat bottom, steeply flaring sides and rounded corners. Even baby carriers were often made of split cedar root. The roots for these baskets were generally dug in spring, heated in the fire, peeled, split, and bundled for later use. Bundles of cedar root were a common trading item amongst Interior Salish peoples. For example, the Shuswap of the Canim Lake area formerly dug the roots in the mountains northeast of the lake, processed them, and sold them at the annual Shuswap tribal gathering at Green Lake. Cedar roots were also used for stitching together birch-bark baskets and birch-bark canoes by groups such as the Shuswap, and were also woven into fishing nets.

The uses of the valuable cedar tree continue. The fibrous bark was stripped off in long sheets and used, without further modification, as roofing and siding for temporary shelters. The Interior Salish used these sheets as a covering for sweathouses, as flooring for houses and birch-bark or dugout canoes, and as a lining for underground food caches. The Shuswap made rough cooking vessels for boiling fish by cutting off a piece of bark about 1.3 m (4 ft) long, folding it, and tying it around the top with a twisted "red willow" branch. The Cowichan and other groups made similar vessels.   The Okanagan used the bark to insulate their tule teepees.

The Sechelt placed it between layers of edible roots, including potatoes and turnips, to prevent them from rotting. The Squamish made canoe bailers from it.   The Haida threaded salmonberry sticks at intervals across the inner surface of large sheets of the bark to keep them flat.   Then they piled them up and weighted them down with stones.   They used them for roofing and sold them to their Mainland neighbours along the Nass River at the price of one blanket for two sheets of bark.   The Cowichan used cedar bark steeped in water for tanning fish hooks.

The most valuable part of the bark was the fibrous inner portion.   This was used by virtually every group having access to the cedar tree, but especially by Coastal peoples.   It split into strips for weaving open- and closed-work baskets, bags, hats, walls, floor and sleeping mats, and capes and blankets, although yellow cedar bark was usually preferred for the latter.   It was twisted into string for making shaman's and dancer's ceremonial headrings, neckrings, armbands and belts, fishing lines, ropes, harpoon lines, animal snares, nets, and for threading clams and fish for drying.   Finely shredded, it was used to make brooms and paint brushes, work aprons, skirts, capes, and dance costumes, for decorating masks, as tinder, napkins, towelling, bandaging, diapers, infant bedding, and for covering the hands of drummers during winter dances. Some Coast Salish groups made a "slow match" by binding a bundle of shredded cedar bark tightly with some less flammable substance.   The inner core was ignited and would smoulder inside its wrapping for many hours.   The Saanich made torches from it. The Stalo Indians of the Fraser Valley combined it with mountain goat wool, dog hair, and bird feathers for spinning.   Larger pieces of the inner bark were used in some areas to make canoe bailers, spoons, and storage bags.

Each group had its own techniques for harvesting and preparing the bark, but the general method remained the same.   Fairly young cedar trees, about 0.3 m (1 ft) in diameter, with few lower branches, were selected.   A transverse cut, several feet from the ground, was made through the bark for about one-quarter or one-

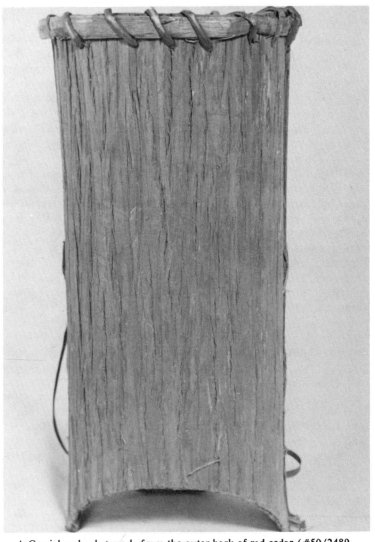

A Cowichan bucket made from the outer bark of red cedar (#50/2489, American Museum of Natural History, New York).

—Dorothy I. D. Kennedy

Kerfed cedar box.

—Harold Hosford

87

plat photo

third the circumference of the tree. The bark was pried up, care being taken not to split it, then grasped at the bottom and pulled outward and upward. The bark strip became narrower as it went higher and finally broke or was jerked off when it reached the crown. It was often 9 m (30 ft) or more in length. The brittle outer bark was pulled off, to be left or bundled and taken home for fuel, and the inner portion, about 0.5 cm (0.2 in.) thick, of a leather-like texture, and light in colour, was folded into an elongated bundle, tied with the thin upper end, and carried home. It might take half a dozen or more of these strips to make a mat or basket.

While still fresh the bark was split into two thinner pieces, the innermost of which was considered of the highest quality. At this stage, the bark could be dried for later processing, or could be split and woven while still fresh. Shredding and softening the fibres was usually accomplished by pounding the bark over the edge of

A Cowichan berry basket of split cedar root with grass imbrication
(#59736, Field Museum of Natural History, Chicago).

—Dorothy I. D. Kennedy

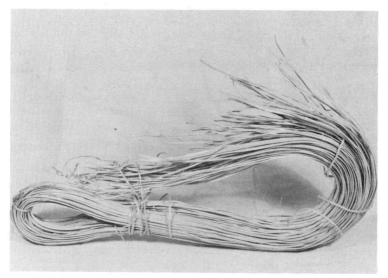

Peeled and split roots of red cedar to be used in Thompson basketry
(#II-C-700, National Museum of Man, Ottawa).

—Dorothy I. D. Kennedy

a paddle or board with a beater of yew wood, stone, or whale bone. Sometimes the bark was submerged in fresh or salt water for several days to soften it. When dry it could be rendered flexible again simply by soaking it. Before a basket, hat, or mat was woven, the long strips of bark were split off and bundled individually in readiness for use. The natural colour of the bark when fully aged is a dark reddish brown. Often strips of bark for weaving, and shredded bark for head and neck rings and for decorating masks, were dyed red with the bark of the red alder, or black with charcoal or by immersion in water in which rusty nails had been soaked. The coloured strands were interwoven with undyed strands to produce patterns and special effects.

PLEASE NOTE—Harvesting cedar bark is harmful to the tree. Even when the trunk is not completely girdled, the wood is exposed to insect and fungal infestations and the capacity of the tree to transport nutrients is reduced. Would-be bark collectors should use the utmost discretion and should choose only trees which are already destined for destruction through land clearing for roads, power-lines, buildings, or agriculture.

Grand Fir and Amabilis Fir	***Abies grandis*(Dougl.) Lindl. and *A. amabilis* (Dougl.) Forbes**
(Pine Family)	**(Pinaceae)**

OTHER NAMES—Grand fir is also called white or balsam fir; amabilis fir is called Pacific silver, silver, Cascade, lovely, or red fir.

BOTANICAL DESCRIPTION—These are both true firs. They are tall, straight trees up to 70 m (230 ft) or more high. The bark when young is smooth, light grey to silvery, and thin, having prominent pitch blisters. It becomes thicker, rougher, and often lighter coloured with age. The needles are dark green above, white on the lower surface, and notched at the tips. *Abies grandis* needles are mostly 2–4 cm (0.8–1.6 in.) long and, especially on young trees, are twisted to lie in a horizontal plane, giving the branches a characteristic flat, spray-like appearance. Those of *A. amabilis* are similar, but, in addition, shorter needles, more or less appressed and pointing forward, are borne along the tops of the twigs. The pollen cones are reddish and pendant from the underside of the upper branches. The seed cones, borne near the top of the tree, are 6–11 cm (2.4–4.3 in.) long, single, cylindrical, and stiffly erect, the scales and bracts being shed with the seeds in the fall, leaving only the central axis on the branch. Those of *A. grandis* are light green, and of *A. amabilis* purplish. The seeds are light brown and have large, membranous wings.

HABITAT—*Abies grandis* grows in damp to moderately dry coniferous forests; *A. amabilis* is found in moist, rich soils in shady bottomlands and montane forests.

DISTRIBUTION IN BRITISH COLUMBIA—*Abies grandis* is found from sea level to moderate elevations on Vancouver Island and the adjacent Mainland, recurring in the valleys of the Kootenay

Grand fir (*Abies grandis*).

—Nancy J. Turner

and Arrow Lakes in the Interior wet belt. *Abies amabilis* grows from sea level to subalpine elevations along the Pacific Coast from Alaska to Vancouver Island, extending inland along some of the major river valleys. Neither species occurs on the Queen Charlotte Islands.

INDIAN USE—The wood of these species, which is soft and rather brittle, was little used, although the Straits Salish made hooks for halibut and dogfish from grand fir, steamed and bent into a horseshoe shape. The Niska sometimes used amabilis fir for house planks. The Chehalis of Washington and probably some British Columbia groups used grand fir wood as a fuel. The Okanagan of the Arrow Lakes region made canoes from grand fir bark, and rubbed the pitch on the backs of bows after they had been wrapped with bitter cherry bark to give them a good grip. The Straits Salish of Vancouver Island made a brown dye for basketry from grand fir bark and a pink dye by combining it with

Koskimo (Kwakiutl) cannibal dancer or 'hamatsa,' with head-dress and wrist-bands of grand fir. Photo by E. S. Curtis, courtesy Provincial Archives of British Columbia.

92

but hemlock usually used.

red ochre. They also rubbed the pitch on canoe paddles and other wooden articles then scorched them to give a good finish.

The boughs of both species have a pleasant spicy fragrance. They were used as bedding, floor coverings, and for covering berry baskets by the Nootka and Thompson, and probably by other groups as well. The Kwakiutl used grand fir branches for ritual scrubbing in purification rites and shamans made costumes and head-dresses from them. The Flathead of Montana dried and pulverized the needles and used them as a baby powder and body scent.

Subalpine Fir	*Abies lasiocarpa* (Hook.) Nutt.
(Pine Family)	**(Pinaceae)**

OTHER NAMES—Alpine, balsam, or white balsam fir; "sweet pine."

BOTANICAL DESCRIPTION—A small tree, usually under 30 m (100 ft) high, with a narrow, spire-shaped crown and short, thick branches. The bark is smooth and ashy-grey. The needles are bluish-green, about 2.5–3.5 cm (1.0–1.4 in.) long, flattened, blunt-tipped on the lower branches, pointed on the upper ones, all crowded and tending to turn upwards. Stomata are borne on both surfaces, in a single whitish median band above and two lateral bands below. The pollen cones are small and bluish, the seed cones usually deep purple, becoming lighter with age, 6–10 cm (2.4–4.0 in.) long, and erect, borne near the top of the tree. The scales are shed with the seeds in the fall, leaving only the central axis. The seeds are light brown with prominent wings.

HABITAT—Moist subalpine forests and open slopes at or near the timberline, where the growth is usually considerably stunted.

DISTRIBUTION IN BRITISH COLUMBIA—Montane forests from the Coast to the Rocky Mountains and from Washington north to Alaska, descending to 600 m (2,000 ft) in the central and northern Interior, common from 1 100 m (3,500 ft) to timberline in the south. Not found on the Queen Charlotte Islands.

Subalpine fir (*Abies lasiocarpa*).

—Nancy J. Turner

INDIAN USE—The soft, even-grained wood was used by the Carrier to make roofing shingles. The rotten wood was burned as a smudge for tanning hides by the Carrier and probably as a general fuel. They also rubbed the pitch on the seams of birch-bark canoes and coated their bowstrings with it. The Shuswap chewed the pitch to clean their teeth. They, and probably other Interior groups, made large temporary baskets from sheets of the bark. These were barrel- or funnel-shaped, with exterior surface of the bark forming the inside of the basket, the seams being stitched with spruce root. They were used for cooking berries or soaking skins and were not considered of as high quality as birch-bark baskets. The boughs, like those of grand fir and amabilis fir, were used as bedding. The Shuswap pushed the broken ends of the branches into the ground to produce a soft, springy sleeping surface. They also used the boughs for flooring in the sweathouse, for standing on after swimming, and as a surface for butchering deer.

The Flathead Salish of Montana placed the fragrant needles on the stove or hung them around the walls of a house to clean and purify the air. They dried and pulverized them to make a baby powder and body and clothing scent. They also mixed them with lard and applied them to the hair as a perfume and green tint. The Blackfoot of Alberta burned the leaves at ceremonials as an incense, and used them as a sachet.

Western Larch   *Larix occidentalis* **Nutt.**

(Pine Family)   **(Pinaceae)**

OTHER NAMES—Tamarack, western tamarack, "red fir."

BOTANICAL DESCRIPTION—A large, handsome tree up to 70 m (230 ft) high with thick, flaky cinnamon-coloured bark and few branches on the lower trunks of mature individuals. The needles are pale green, 2.5–4.5 cm (1.0–1.8 in.) long, in clusters of 15 to 30. Unlike most conifer needles, they are deciduous, turning golden yellow and shedding in autumn. The yellowish pollen cones are about 1 cm (0.4 in.) long, and the seed cones 2.5–4.0 cm (1.0–1.6 in.) long, at first purplish-red, later reddish-brown.

HABITAT—Mountain valleys and lower slopes, in open, dry to moist habitats, usually in mixed stands.

DISTRIBUTION IN BRITISH COLUMBIA—On north slopes and in higher valleys of the Kootenay, Arrow, and Okanagan drainage systems, from the United States border north as far as Shuswap Lake.

INDIAN USE—The wood is rather difficult to work, and was seldom used by native people. The Thompson and Okanagan heated the pitch in the fire until it was hard and dry, then pounded it with a stone or a mortar and pestle into a fine reddish powder. Girls from about age 9 to 16 would mix this with grease and smear it on their faces as a cosmetic and skin conditioner. A general purpose red paint for colouring wood, buckskin, and other materials was made by mixing the powder with cottonwood bud resin to make a sticky paste. From descriptions of the location of some of the trees used—between Hope and Princeton in the vicinity of Manning Park—it is possible that the alpine larch (*L. lyallii* Parl.) was also used. The Flathead of Montana used larch sap to plaster the hair in place. According to Okanagan tradition, when larch trees turn yellow in the fall, it is a sign that pregnant female bears are retiring to their dens for the winter; it was also believed that if larch needles fell on the rump of a pregnant bear she would have a miscarriage.

Engelmann Spruce and White Spruce	*Picea engelmannii* Parry ex Engelm. and *P. glauca* (Moench) Voss
(Pine Family)	**(Pinaceae)**

BOTANICAL DESCRIPTION—Engelmann spruce is a straight, spire-shaped tree up to 50 m (165 ft) tall, while white spruce is usually less than 25 m (80 ft) tall, and is often deformed and stunted. The bark of Engelmann spruce is brownish-red and scaly; that of white spruce is silvery-brown, also scaly. The needles of both are bluish-green, slender, sharp, and four-sided, tending to project from all sides of the twigs, or commonly turning

Engelmann spruce (*Picea engelmannii*).

—Steve Cannings

upward. The pollen cones of Engelmann spruce are yellow, those of white spruce reddish. The seed cones of Engelmann spruce are 4–5 cm (1.6–2.0 in.) long, yellowish-brown to purplish-brown, the scales thin with wavy margins; those of white spruce are 2.5–3.5 cm (1.0–1.4 in.) long, light brown to purplish, the scales usually stiffer, blunter, and more regular than those of Engelmann spruce. These two species are closely related and commonly hybridize in areas where their ranges overlap. They are often treated as geographic races of the same species, Engelmann spruce being designated *P. glauca* ssp. *engelmannii* Taylor, and white spruce *P. glauca* ssp. *glauca*. To distinguish between them is very difficult; the shape of the cone scales is probably the best indication.

HABITAT—Both species are highly frost-resistant, white spruce even more so than Engelmann spruce. The latter grows in damp, shady subalpine forests, in upland swamps, and alluvial floodplains; the former generally occurs in damp boreal forests, swamps, and floodplains, usually at lower elevations than Engelmann spruce.

DISTRIBUTION IN BRITISH COLUMBIA—Engelmann spruce occurs mainly east of the Coast and Cascade Mountains to the Rockies, south of latitude 51°31′N. and above 900 m (3,000 ft) elevation, but does appear sporadically further north and at lower elevations. White spruce is widespread in the northern Interior forests, extending south to the Interior Plateau and eastward into the Rocky Mountain Trench.

INDIAN USE—These species are seldom clearly distinguished by Indian people and are therefore treated together. It seems likely that Engelmann spruce was the species commonly used by the groups of the southern Interior, while white spruce was used by the northern Interior peoples.

The Tahltan used the wood from spruce saplings to make snowshoe frames, but considered it somewhat heavy and brittle, and not durable. They also used it for gambling sticks and sometimes for bows. They heated the gum and used it to glue skin onto bows and arrowheads onto shafts. The decayed wood they used for tanning hides. The Carrier used a type of spruce wood to make the encircling pieces for fish traps, but this may have been black spruce [*Picea mariana* (Mill.) B.S.P.], which they sometimes employed for snowshoe frames and drying poles. Spruce roots, peeled, split, and soaked in water, were used throughout the Interior for sewing the seams and rims of birch bark and other types of bark baskets. The Interior Salish and Athapaskan peoples used them, like red cedar roots, to make tightly woven coiled baskets; in fact the Shuswap, Carrier, and Chilcotin used them even more than cedar roots for this purpose.

Sheets of spruce bark were stripped off and used by many Interior peoples to make large cooking baskets, similar in style to birch-bark baskets, but not as well finished. The seams and tops were stitched with spruce root. Additionally, the Thompson, Shuswap, and Kootenay made canoes of spruce bark; the Thompson used it for roofing; the Lillooet for baby carriers and as covering for summer lodges; and the Carrier to make trays for gathering and rendering berries.

Shuswap hunters used spruce boughs for bedding, covering them with a thick layer of fir branches as protection against the sharp foliage. Shuswap children learned that if they became lost to always look for a spruce tree for shelter; the thick, hanging branches afforded considerable protection from the elements. Carrier people, when camping, used to strip the spruce needles from the boughs to make a floor covering for tents.

Sitka Spruce

Picea sitchensis
(Bong.) Carr.

(Pine Family)

(Pinaceae)

BOTANICAL DESCRIPTION—A large tree up to 67–70 m (200–230 ft) tall, and 2 m (6 ft) or more in diameter. The bark is thin and grayish with long deciduous scales about 5 cm (2 in.) across. The branches are characteristically droopy and the needles are stiff and sharp-pointed, diamond shaped in cross-section, about 2.5 cm (1 in.) long, tending to project from all sides of the twig. The cones are pale brown, about 6 cm (2.5 in.) long, and hanging. The cone scales are thin, with wavy margins.

HABITAT—A forest tree of the humid west Coast, from sea level to about 600 m (2,000 ft) elevation.

DISTRIBUTION IN BRITISH COLUMBIA—Generally confined to an 80 km (50 mi.) wide Coastal strip. Especially common on the Queen Charlotte Islands and the west coast of Vancouver Island.

INDIAN USE—Sitka spruce wood, though light and strong, was little used by Coastal Indian peoples. The Kwakiutl sometimes

Sitka spruce (*Picea sitchensis*).

—Nancy J. Turner

used it to make digging sticks and slat armour, and the Haida used both wood and bark for fuel. Both of these groups, and probably others as well, made cod and halibut hooks from spruce knots and branches, first steaming them to make them easier to mold. The Makah of Washington made wedges from the wood of the larger roots. The Niska sometimes split house boards from the trunks. To produce extra wide boards for the houses of wealthy and important people, curved pieces were cut from the circumference of the largest trees, then steamed and weighted until flat.

The Nootka and Kwakiutl used spruce gum for cementing implements such as harpoons and spears and for caulking canoes. For hunting porpoise, the Kwakiutl greased their canoes with spruce scented tallow to mask any human odour.

The roots were an important basket material among Coastal peoples. They were also used for making nets, for "sewing" wood such as in box construction, and as a single or multi-ply rope for tying on house planks, binding fish hooks and harpoons, and as

Bella Coola basket of split Sitka spruce root (#VIID 287,
National Museum of Man, Ottawa).

—Dorothy I. D. Kennedy

fishing line and harpoon line. The Niska used them to stitch the rims of their birch-bark baskets. For basketry they were harvested in early summer, from trees with few lower branches and growing in sandy soil, since those in rocky soil produce twisted and knotted roots. Great care was taken in selecting the longest, straightest roots, and different sizes were chosen depending on their intended use. They were tied in individual bundles, then briefly scorched over a hot fire, enough to heat the wood of the root, but not to burn through the bark. If this were not done correctly, the root would soon turn brown. Each root was pulled through a split stick or an upright set of fire tongs to remove the bark and was carefully split along the vertical plane where the line of small secondary rootlets appeared. Depending on the size of the root and its potential use, each half might be split again, yielding two flat strands and two rounded ones. These were pulled over a

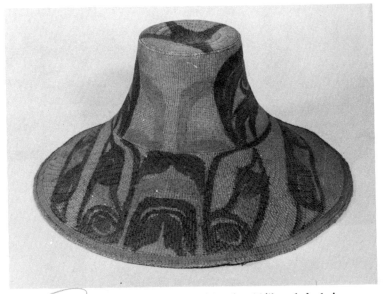

A Haida hat of Sitka spruce root, with painted killer whale design (#2-10294, R. H. Lowie Museum of Anthropology, Berkeley).

—Dorothy I. D. Kennedy

knife blade or some other flat object until they were completely flexible, then dried. They could be made workable again simply by soaking them.

Spruce-root baskets, both closely twined and of open-work weave, were made by most Coastal groups, but the northern people—especially the Haida and the Tlingit of Alaska—were exceptionally skilled in their manufacture. So finely and tightly did they twine the roots that the baskets could be used to pack water, and when held to the light not a leak could be seen. Watertight spruce-root hats were another specialty of these people. Sometimes baskets and hats were decorated by imbrication or by weaving in dyed strands of material, but the Haida and Tlingit preferred to paint designs on the finished products, using charcoal and natural mineral paints.

Lodgepole Pine	*Pinus contorta*
	Dougl. ex Loud.
(Pine Family)	**(Pinaceae)**

OTHER NAMES—Shore pine, scrub pine, "jack pine," "black pine," "red pine."

BOTANICAL DESCRIPTION—A small to medium tree, rounded or pyramidal, mostly 10–28 m (35–90 ft) high, with thin limbs often confined to the top third of the tree in crowded conditions. The bark is thin, rough, reddish-brown to greyish-black, and scaly. The needles are in groups of two, 3–6 cm (1.2–2.4 in.) long, often with a yellowish-green tinge. The pollen cones are small, strongly clustered, and reddish-green. The woody seed cones are oval-shaped and usually slightly lop-sided, tending to remain closed on the tree for many years, some opening only after a hot fire.

HABITAT—A highly adaptable species, found from Coastal dunes and bogs to rocky hilltops and upland plains, often forming pure stands.

DISTRIBUTION IN BRITISH COLUMBIA—Widespread throughout the Province from sea level to subalpine elevations, especially common as a successional species in burned-over forests east of the Cascades.

Lodgepole pine (*Pinus contorta*).

—Robert D. Turner

INDIAN USE—The wood is soft, light, and straight-grained, but is weak and not very durable. As the name suggests, this tree was commonly used to make teepee poles and other types by the Okanagan and Thompson, as well as by the Flathead of Montana and the Blackfoot of Alberta. The poles were usually cut in summer, debarked, trimmed, and sun-dried. The Lillooet have recently used the trunks to build log cabins. The Tahltan sometimes made arrow shafts from the wood, and the Kwakiutl used it to make fire tongs, board protectors for bending boards, cedar-bark peelers, digging sticks, and harpoon shafts. The wood, being very pitchy, was said by the Shuswap to burn even when green, and was a major source of fuel for hunters and travellers. The Carrier made fire drills from it, and the Lillooet used it to make torches. The Tahltan used the decayed wood as a smudge for tanning hides.

Other parts of the tree were also used. The Niska occasionally split and twisted the roots for rope. The Haida employed sheets of the bark as splints for broken limbs, and the Lillooet sometimes used them for covering summer lodges. The Tahltan strewed the boughs on the floors of their houses. The pitch, a highly versatile substance, was used by the Sechelt to waterproof canoes and baskets and to make a hot fire, by the Saanich to fasten arrowheads onto shafts, and by the Lower Lillooet to seal fish hooks, and, mixed with bear grease and heated, to provide a protective coating for Indian hemp fishing line and to glue bitter cherry bark over the joints of harpoons and other implements. The Thompson also mixed it with grease and rubbed it on the outside of stone pipes to give them a smooth, glossy finish.

White Pine

Pinus monticola
Dougl. ex D. Don

(Pine Family)

(Pinaceae)

OTHER NAME—Western white pine.

BOTANICAL DESCRIPTION—A slender, attractive, medium-sized tree, usually under 30 m (100 ft) tall. The bark is thin and greyish when young, becoming thicker and checking into rectangular flaking scales with age. The needles are in bundles of 5, bluish-green, slender, and 5–10 cm (2–4 in.) long. The pollen cones are yellowish and clustered, usually under 1 cm (0.4 in.) long. The seed cones, borne on the upper branches, are pendant and cylindrical, 15–25 cm (6–10 in.) long and 6–9 cm (2.4–3.5 in.) thick at maturity. The scales are green to purplish when young, turning brownish

White pine (*Pinus monticola*).

—Robert D. Turner

with age, and often tipped with large globules of white pitch. The seeds are 7–10 mm (0.3–0.4 in.) long, with wings 2 to 3 times as long.

HABITAT—Well-drained, sandy soils in valley bottoms to open slopes up to 1 800 m (6,000 ft) on the Coast and about 1 100 m (3,500 ft) in the Interior.

DISTRIBUTION IN BRITISH COLUMBIA—On Vancouver Island and the adjacent Mainland, east to Manning Park in the Cascades; common in the Interior wet belt, south to the American border and north to Quesnel Lake.

INDIAN USE—The wood is light and moderately strong and durable, but was seldom used in carving or construction. However, the Manhousat Nootka used it to make long mat needles, and reportedly named the tree after this use.

The bark was peeled off in large sheets and used by the Shuswap, Kootenay, and Arrow Lakes Okanagan, and, rarely, by the Lillooet and the Skagit of Washington, to make storage baskets and small canoes. George Dawson reported that as of 1891 pine-bark canoes were still occasionally used on Shuswap Lake near the Columbia River. As with birch bark, the inner side of the bark became the outer side of the canoe. The seams were sewn with roots and the inside was strengthened with wooden ribs and cross-braces which were lashed in place. Knot-holes and fissures were plugged with resin. Pine-bark canoes were said to be very swift and, when balanced properly, remarkably seaworthy. Pine-bark baskets were made in the same fashion as those of birch bark, being stitched with roots and strengthened at the top with withes. The Sechelt sometimes used white pine pitch for waterproofing.

Ponderosa Pine   *Pinus ponderosa*
                                                     Dougl. ex Loud.
(Pine Family)   **(Pinaceae)**

OTHER NAMES—Yellow pine, bull pine.

BOTANICAL DESCRIPTION—A large forest tree, commonly 30 m (100 ft) or more high, with thick, reddish, furrowed bark which flakes off in irregular scales. The yellowish-green needles, usually in clusters of three, are longer than those of any other conifer in British Columbia, frequently exceeding 20 cm (8 in.) in length. They are usually borne clustered toward the branch ends, giving the entire tree a feathery appearance. The pollen cones are yellow to purplish and strongly clustered, and the female or seed cones are broadly oval-shaped, reddish-purple when young, and brown when they mature, after two years. The seeds are 6–7 mm (0.24–0.28 in.) long, with prominent wings to aid in dispersal.

HABITAT—Dry warm valleys and slopes up to 900 m (3,000 ft). Intolerant of shade and extreme cold temperatures.

DISTRIBUTION IN BRITISH COLUMBIA—Forming open park-like forests in the dry southern Interior of British Columbia east of the Cascade Mountains, from the Fraser and Thompson River Canyons to the Okanagan and Similkameen Valleys, as far north as Clinton in the Cariboo; recurring in the dry sections of the Kootenay and Columbia Valleys.

INDIAN USE—The Southern Okanagan and Fraser River Thompson often made dugout canoes from this tree. The wood is heavier than cedar wood, and said to split more easily. Additionally, the Okanagan used it for cache poles. The wood, bark, and cones were valued by all southern Interior peoples as a fuel. The Okanagan used the wood as a hearth for making friction fires, and made the drill from a dried-out section of the leading shoot from the last year's growth. The Shuswap burned the wood, the bark, and the pitchy tops of this pine on camping trips, because it burned fast and cooled quietly, so that enemies could not tell how long ago the camp had been broken. They and the Okanagan used the rotten wood for smoking hides, while the Thompson used the cones for this purpose, often mixing them with Douglas-fir bark. The Okanagan used the spiny, immature cones for "combing" out the fibres of Indian hemp stems. Finished Indian hemp fishing lines were rubbed with ponderosa pine gum to help preserve them, as were various fishing implements which were bound with Indian hemp twine.

Ponderosa pine boughs have a spicy fragrance and were used generally as bedding and for covering floors. They were especially

Ponderosa pine (*Pinus ponderosa*), showing dry habitat with
balsamroot and bunchgrass.

—Nancy J. Turner

useful in doorways and on paths during the winter because they promoted rapid melting of the snow. The needles were used as insulation for cellars, food caches, and underground storage pits, and when dry were employed as tinder. The Shuswap formerly gathered the pollen in springtime, mixed it with hot water, and dyed clothing a light yellow colour with this concoction.

Douglas-fir	*Pseudotsuga menziesii* (Mirbel) Franco
(Pine Family)	**(Pinaceae)**

OTHER NAMES—Oregon pine, simply "fir" to many Indian people.

BOTANICAL DESCRIPTION—A giant forest tree up to 70 m (230 ft) high on the Coast, but seldom more than 40 m (130 ft) in the Interior. The bark of young trees is smooth and grey-brown, often with resin-blisters, while on old trees it becomes thick and fur-rowed, grey outside and mottled red-brown and whitish inside. The needles are flat, pointed but not prickly, about 2.5 cm (1 in.) long, uniformly spaced along the twig and spreading from the sides and top. The pollen cones are small and reddish-brown, and the seed cones, which hang from the branches, are green before maturity, then reddish-brown to grey and soon falling. Prominent 3-pointed bracts extend well beyond the cone scales. Cones of Coastal trees are at most 6–10 cm (2.4–4.0 in.) long, while those of Interior trees vary from 4–7 cm (1.5–2.8 in.). The seeds are 5–6 mm (0.20–0.23 in.), with prominent wings. Coastal and Interior populations form two well-defined geographic races, desig-nated as *P. menziesii* var. *menziesii* and *P. menziesii* var. *glauca* (Beissn.) Franco respectively.

HABITAT—Moist to very dry areas, from sea level to 1 050 m (3,500 ft) in the southern Interior, and as high as 1 800 m (6,000 ft) in the Rockies.

DISTRIBUTION IN BRITISH COLUMBIA—Widespread throughout the southern half of the Province, extending as far north as Stuart and McLeod Lakes and up the Parnsip River in the Interior.

Does not occur on the Queen Charlotte Islands or most of the central and northern Coast.

INDIAN USE—Douglas-fir wood is heavy, strong, fine-grained, and durable. It works well and seasons fairly easily. It was used by the Okanagan to make teepee poles, drying scaffolds, smoking racks, and spear shafts, and by the Shuswap for spear shafts, gaff-hook poles, canoe cross-braces, and river poles, although cedar was a preferred material for these items. Okanagan ice fishermen blackened their Douglas-fir spears in the fire to make them invisible to fish. One Shuswap man reportedly made a fir-wood dugout canoe, which lasted for many years. The Carrier used Douglas-fir for making fish traps and, along with the Shuswap and Kootenay, made snowshoes from it. The Lillooet used forked Douglas-fir saplings to make dipnet frames, molding them to a circular shape while still green. They also made harpoon shafts from the branches, as did the Katzie (Stalo), the Squamish, and various other Coastal Salish groups. Spoons, spear shafts, dipnet

Douglas-fir (*Pseudotsuga menziesii*).

—Nancy J. Turner

111

poles, harpoon barbs, fire tongs, and salmon weirs were frequently made from fir wood by the Coast Salish and, at least on Vancouver Island, the Salish people molded halibut and cod hooks from fir knots, as well as those of hemlock, by steaming them, placing them in a section of bull kelp stipe overnight to give them the right curvature, then drying them and rubbing them with tallow to waterproof them. The Kwakiutl sometimes made coffins of fir wood. The Comox prepared dogfish flesh by stuffing it with powdered rotten Douglas-fir wood and burying it for a period of time in a pit lined with the same material.

Virtually all Coastal groups within the range of the tree considered Douglas-fir wood and bark to be an excellent fuel. The Bella Coola, Lillooet, and Quinault of Washington made torches from the pitchy heartwood, and the Vancouver Island Salish and Flathead of Montana used the rotten wood to smoke hides. The Thompson mixed fir bark with ponderosa pine cones for this purpose.

The fragrant boughs were used throughout the southern Interior as flooring for the sweathouse and for covering the outside of sweathouses, as well as for covering temporary shelters, as flooring for houses, for covering ice-fishing holes, for shading fish and berries on drying racks, as matting for sitting, drying food, and butchering deer on, as scrubbers for initiates and hunters, as padding for packs, and as bedding. For this last purpose up to six layers of boughs were used. Fir boughs were often spread over layers of other less desirable types of boughs. The Shuswap used fir branches tied in loose knots and suspended from tree limbs as targets for shooting arrows. Young Shuswap men bound bundles of the branches on their feet and ran through the water with them to exercise their leg muscles.

The Okanagan added fir needles to water in which split cedar roots for weaving were soaking to impart a yellow tint to the roots. The Swinomish of Washington boiled the bark to make a light brown dye for fish nets, making them invisible to fish. The pitch was used by many groups within the range of the tree for sealing the joints of implements such as harpoon heads, gaff hooks, and fish hooks, and for caulking canoes and water vessels. The Lillooet mixed it with earth and sand to make soles for fish-skin moccasins.

Western Hemlock

Tsuga heterophylla (Raf.) Sarg.

(Pine Family)

(Pinaceae)

BOTANICAL DESCRIPTION—An evergreen tree, 30–50 m (100–165 ft) tall and 1 m (about 3 ft) in diameter. The crown is narrow, and the top and branches drooping, especially in young trees. The bark is thick and deeply furrowed in older trees, and dark brown to reddish-brown. The needles are unequal in length, varying between 8 and 20 mm (0.3 and 0.8 in.), flattened, blunt, white beneath in two bands, and usually spread at right angles to the twigs, so that the branches are flattened. Cones are numerous, about 2 cm (0.8 in.) long, annual, purplish to green when young and light brown when ripe, opening widely at maturity.

HABITAT—Western hemlock grows best in humid climates and its shade tolerance is one of the highest among our conifers.

DISTRIBUTION IN BRITISH COLUMBIA—Common along the entire British Columbia Coast to moderate elevations in the mountains where it is replaced by the mountain hemlock [*T. mertensiana* (Bong.) Carr.]. It recurs in the Interior wet belt west of the Rocky Mountains, as far north as the Parsnip River.

INDIAN USE—Hemlock wood, which is moderately heavy and durable and works fairly easily, was used generally along the Coast to carve implements such as spoons, roasting spits, dipnet poles, combs, spear shafts, and elderberry-picking hooks. The Haida and Straits Salish made C-shaped halibut and cod hooks from the knots formed by the ends of the limbs in rotten hemlock stumps. These were barbed with bone or iron, and the ends were sprung apart with a small stick, which was released when a fish was caught, and which then floated to the surface as an indicator of the fisherman's success. The wood from bent trunks was used by the Haida to carve large feast dishes. Fishing weirs, wedges,

Western hemlock (*Tsuga heterophylla*).

—Nancy J. Turner

114

devil-fish spears, children's bows, and ridgepoles for portable houses were also made by these people. They sometimes spliced the roots onto bull kelp fishing lines to strengthen them. The Niska used hemlock twigs to make rims for their birch-bark baskets.

Hemlock bark, which has a high tannin content, was prepared in various ways for use as a tanning agent, pigment, and cleansing solution. The Saanich, a Straits Salish group, and other Coast Salish peoples pounded and boiled it in fresh water to make a reddish dye for colouring mountain goat wool and basket materials. Young women of this group rubbed the dye on their faces as a cosmetic and reportedly to remove facial hair. The Kwakiutl steeped the bark in urine to make a black eye, and the Bella Coola used a water solution of it to colour fish nets brown, making them invisible to fish. They also rubbed the liquid on traps to remove rust and give them a clean scent. In Washington State, the Clallam, Lummi, and Makah pounded the inner bark and boiled it in salt water to make a red paint and wood preservative for spears and paddles. It was said to be more effective when baked on over a fire. The Snohomish used the dye to colour basket materials and the Chehalis to tint fish nets. The Quinault mashed the bark with salmon eggs to obtain a yellow-orange paint for staining dipnets and paddles. The Quileute used a solution of it for tanning hides and for soaking spruce-root baskets to make them watertight.

Hemlock branches were considered an excellent bedding material, and were frequently used along the Coast for collecting herring spawn. During the spawning season, from March to June, the boughs were tied in bundles and lowered into the ocean near river estuaries. Later they were gathered and the spawn scraped off and eaten fresh or dried. The Mainland Comox threaded eulachon and herring on hemlock boughs for drying, and also used the branches to line steam-cooking pits. The Squamish used them as "rags" to wipe the slime off fish. Kwakiutl hunters walking through the forest made trail markers by breaking hemlock branches and turning them back to show the conspicuous white underside. Dancers and novitiates of this group wore skirts, head-

Herring eggs on boughs of western hemlock. The clear eggs are
uncooked; the white, cooked (collected by D. W. Ellis).

—Robert D. Turner

dresses, and head-bands of hemlock boughs, and pubescent girls
lived in hemlock bough huts for four days after their first menstru-
ation. Hemlock gum, like that of other conifers, was sometimes
used as a glue for fastening implements together.

Western Yew	***Taxus brevifolia* Nutt.**
(Yew Family)	**(Taxaceae)**

OTHER NAME—Pacific yew.

BOTANICAL DESCRIPTION—A small, shrub-like tree, 5–15 m
(16–45 ft) high, and up to 30 cm (12 in.) in diameter, often
twisted and leaning. The bark is reddish, thin, and scaly. The wood
is strong and flexible, and was widely utilized on the Coast for
making implements. Needles are flattened, about 15–20 mm
(0.6–0.8 in.) long, brownish-green, with pointed tips, and 2-ranked.
The branches superficially resemble hemlock branches but are

Western yew (*Taxus brevifolia*).

—Nancy J. Turner

green beneath, rather than whitish. Male and female reproductive structures are borne on different trees. Male trees produce minute, yellowish staminate cones, and female trees bear round, pinkish-red fruits, consisting of a hard brown seed surrounded by a fleshy cup. These "berries" are borne on the underside of the branches, and ripen in September.

HABITAT—Sporadic in moist forests, most commonly found along streams and damp slopes.

DISTRIBUTION IN BRITISH COLUMBIA—Common on the Pacific Coast to the Cascade Mountains, and recurring in the Interior wet belt (the Selkirk Mountains and Rocky Mountain Trench).

INDIAN USE—The heavy, close-grained wood of the yew is well known for its strength and durability. It was prized by all native peoples within the range of the tree, and was frequently traded into areas of the Interior where it did not occur naturally. It was used to make implements such as bows, wedges, clubs, paddles, digging sticks, prying sticks, adze handles, and harpoon shafts which were required to withstand considerable stress. Although tough and hard, it carves fairly easily, taking a high polish. As an indication of its importance as a carving material, yew is called "bow plant" or "bow" in a number of Indian languages, including Haida, Halkomelem, and Lillooet, and "wedge plant" in Sechelt, Squamish, and Nootka. Even the Shuswap in the Interior made bows from it, although yew is fairly scarce in their territory. They and the Upper Thompson often obtained the wood from the Lillooet and Lower Thompson. The Flathead Salish of Montana also made yew bows, seasoning the wood well and varnishing the finished product with boiled sinew to waterproof it and prevent it from warping. The Saanich of Vancouver Island molded the ends of their bows to the proper curvature by steaming them inside a length of bull kelp stipe. Some groups, such as the Niska, backed their yew bows with sinew.

Kwakiutl digging stick of western yew (Ethnology Division, British Columbia Provincial Museum).

A Squamish wedge of yew wood (#VIIG 210 National Museum of Man, Ottawa).

—Dorothy I. D. Kennedy

118

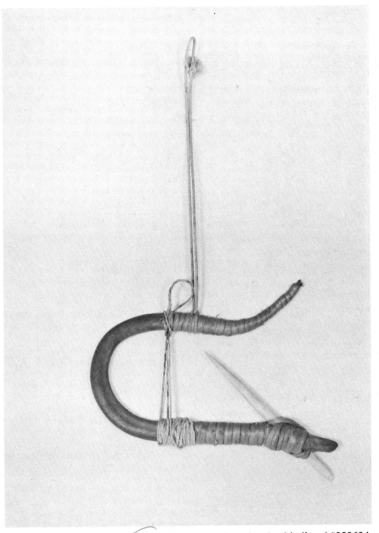

A Nootka halibut hook of yew, with bone barb and cedar binding (#289694, Smithsonian Institution, Washington, D.C.).

—Dorothy I. D. Kennedy

rarely if ever used —according to ... —Friedman

Yew wood was also used to make a variety of other objects, including mat-sewing needles, awls, dipnet frames, halibut and other types of fish hooks, knives, dishes, spoons, spears and spear-points, boxes, dowels and pegs, drum frames, canoe spreaders, bark scrapers, canoe bailers, fire tongs, combs, and gambling sticks. The Lillooet considered it the best possible material for snowshoe frames, and recently employed it to make shovel and axe handles. In all cases, the red-coloured heartwood was preferred for carving to the white sapwood. Native wood carvers still like to use yew, but often have difficulty obtaining large enough pieces. While yew is little-used commercially, it is seldom an abundant species, and past harvesting by carvers combined with habitat destruction through logging has greatly reduced the numbers of large old yew trees in many localities.

The entire trunk was employed as an implement for warfare by the Saanich. They would fit a spear to a yew sapling, pull it back, and release it as an effective catapult. Additionally, Saanich women used yew twigs to remove under-arm hair. The Kwakiutl bound a bundle of yew branches to a hemlock pole to make a tool for gathering sea urchins; the spines of these animals became entangled in the branches. Young Kwakiutl men tested their strength by trying to twist a yew tree from crown to butt. The Quinault of Washington used a yew trunk as the spring rod in a deer trap, and the Lillooet used the branches to support deer-hide hammocks. Finally, the Okanagan ground dry yew wood and mixed it with fish oil to make a red paint.

FLOWERING PLANTS (ANGIOSPERMAE)
MONOCOTYLEDONS

Skunk Cabbage

(Arum Family)

Lysichitum americanum
Hultén & St. John

(Araceae)

OTHER NAME—Yellow arum.

BOTANICAL DESCRIPTION—A perennial herb, with thick, fleshy rootstocks and large, oval-shaped, clustered leaves, mostly 4 to 10 dm (15–40 in.) long, bright green, and waxy. "Flowers" appear in early spring, consisting of a yellow sheath, up to 2 dm (8 in.) long, surrounding a yellowish-green club-like flower stalk. At maturity, the stalk breaks apart to reveal brown, oval seeds embedded in a white, pulpy tissue. The skunk-like odour of this plant resembles that of the closely related *Symplocarpus foetidus* (L.) Nutt. of eastern North America.

HABITAT—In swampy ground, especially black mucky soil, beneath red alder and conifers; rarely flowers in dense shade.

DISTRIBUTION IN BRITISH COLUMBIA—Common in Coastal forests, Vancouver Island to Alaska, and east to the Columbia River, but not in arid or semi-arid areas.

INDIAN USE—The large, flat, water-repellent leaves are aptly referred to by some native people as "Indian waxed paper." They filled the role of waxed paper in virtually all Coastal Indian cultures and even in some areas of the Interior. They were widely employed for such tasks as lining steam-cooking pits and covering food being cooked in them, lining and covering berry baskets, lining storage

Skunk cabbage (*Lysichitum americanum*).

—Robert D. Turner

pits, such as for "stink salmon eggs," laying under food, wrapping salmon for cooking, lining oil boxes to prevent leakage, and drying berries and other food on. For this last, the fleshy mid-ribs were removed and the leaves were laid overlapping on the ground or on a wooden rack. Then rectangular wooden frames were set over them and the berries, which were usually cooked to a jam-like consistency, were poured into the frames and allowed to dry. Later the leaves were simply peeled off the bottom of the berry cake and it was stored. Although they have a decidedly acrid odour, the leaves did not seem to impart any unpleasant taste to the foods they came in contact with.

The Bella Coola and other Coast Salish peoples made an ingenious temporary drinking cup and water dipper by folding a large skunk cabbage leaf in half from top to bottom and pulling the edges back to the lower end, holding them together with the stem as a handle. They also constructed makeshift berry containers by pinning the leaf edges together with sticks. The Squamish used the larger leaves for sun shades on hot summer days.

Sedges   *Carex obnupta* **L. and other *Carex* species**

(Sedge Family)   **(Cyperaceae)**

OTHER NAMES—"Swamp grass," "Swamp hay," tall basket sedge.

BOTANICAL DESCRIPTION—Sedges are fibrous-rooted, often rhizomatous herbs which resemble grasses in overall aspect. The stems are usually triangular in cross-section or sometimes rounded, and the leaves are tough, mostly 3-ranked with closed (or rarely open) sheaths, with parallel-veined, typically elongated and grass-like blades. The plants are wind pollinated. The individual flowers are generally reduced and inconspicuous, borne in spikes or spikelets and subtended by small, brownish scales. The male staminate structures and female pistillate structures are often borne on different sections of the same spike, on different spikes, or even on different plants. The flower spikes are often clustered into compact or open heads, which are frequently subtended by elongated leaf-like bracts.

122

Sedge or "swamp grass" (*Carex obnupta*).

—Nancy J. Turner

Carex obnupta is a relatively large sedge, densely tufted, with long, creeping rhizomes and coarse, stout stems mostly 6–15 dm (2–5 ft) tall, with conspicuous reddish-brown basal membranes. The leaves are coarse and stiff, the blades mostly 3–10 mm (0.1–0.4 in.) wide, and more or less V-shaped in cross-section. The inflorescence, or flower-head, is subtended usually by 3 bracts, which are sheathless and elongated, the lowest one usually 10–50 cm (4–20 in.) long, and the others progressively reduced. The spikes, from 4 to 8, cylindrical, and drooping or spreading are mostly 5–12 cm (2–5 in.) long. The upper 1–3 spikes are staminate, producing pollen, the others entirely or partially pistillate. The pistillate scales are narrow, pointed, and dark brown with a pale midrib.

HABITAT—Sedges are most common in moist or wet places, but some species occur in moderately dry to semi-arid sites. *Carex obnupta* is found in wet meadows and marshes along lake margins, rivers, or occasionally in saline coastal swamps.

DISTRIBUTION IN BRITISH COLUMBIA—There are well over 100 different species of *Carex* in British Columbia, occurring throughout the Province from sea level to alpine elevations. *Carex obnupta* grows west of the Coast and Cascade Mountains from the Queen Charlotte Islands south to Vancouver Island and the adjacent Mainland. It is one of the most common and widely distributed lowland sedges in the western part of the Province.

INDIAN USE—Several different sedges were used in Indian technology in British Columbia, but it has been difficult to identify them exactly because most Indian people do not distinguish taxonomically between different species of sedges having the same general growth habit. Often sedges are simply classed in a general category with grasses and other grass-like plants.

Carex obnupta was and still is a popular basket material for the Nootka on the west coast of Vancouver Island, as well as the Makah of Washington. The Hesquiat people, north of Tofino, are making a concerted effort to revive and preserve the many facets of their cultural heritage, including weaving with "swamp grass" (*C. obnupta*). The author had the privilege of helping to prepare some of the leaves for weaving in the traditional manner. The plants are

124

gathered during the summer from swampy meadows north of Hesquiat Village. Only the vegetative or "female" plants are used. Anyone harvesting the fruiting or "male" plants is laughed at. The clusters of leaves are pulled up from the tender white bases, where they break off at or just below the ground level. They are then tied in large bundles and taken back to the village, where the outer leaves are discarded and the inner ones peeled off and split exactly in two lengthwise by running the thumbnail along the midrib. Pieces not split exactly in half are discarded. Each half is then run through the closed thumb and fore-finger to flatten it and make it flexible. One must be careful during the operation not to get cut, because the leaf edges are extremely sharp. The processed halves are tied in bundles of several dozen each by their lower ends and hung up to dry, outside if the weather permits, or inside if it is raining. When dry, the bundles are stored for weaving in the fall and winter. The finest baskets, often with cedar-bark foundations, are made from this "grass" by a twining process. Intricate patterns

Mrs. Mike Tom of Hesquiat, Vancouver Island, splitting the leaves of tall basket sedge (*Carex obnupta*) in preparation for drying.

—Nancy J. Turner

Tall basket sedge bundled and hung to dry at Hesquiat.

—Nancy J. Turner

and designs are achieved by weaving in dyed strands of the "grass" or by superimposing dyed or naturally coloured materials over the regular weave. Many different styles and sizes of baskets are woven, the most common being round with a flat bottom and fitted lid. After the coming of Europeans it became a widespread practice to weave around bottles and dishes in less traditional forms. Aniline dyes of brightest hue almost entirely replaced the soft tones of natural pigments in the designs.

The Squamish, Sechelt, Haida, and other Coastal groups also used *Carex obnupta* for weaving, and employed other sedges as well, such as *C. lyngbyei* Hornem., a common species of Coastal marshes and tidal flats. In the Interior, the Okanagan used *Carex concinnoides* Mack., a small sedge of dry to moderately moist coniferous forests, for laying over and under food in steaming pits, for lining moccasins, and for covering and lining berry baskets. The leaves were tied onto a stick to make a beater for soapberries and were sometimes twisted into cord. Recently they were mixed with mud and used to chink log cabins and as mortar for making chimneys. At least one Okanagan informant identified this species as "timbergrass," a plant used throughout the Interior for making soapberry beaters and drying berries on, but informants in other areas identified "timbergrass" as a true grass [*see* pinegrass (*Calamagrostis rubescens*) in Poaceae].

Tule   ***Scirpus acutus* Muhl. ex Bigel.**

(Sedge Family)   **(Cyperaceae)**

OTHER NAMES—Hardstem bulrush, bulrush, rush.

BOTANICAL DESCRIPTION—A stout, rhizomatous perennial usually 1–3 m (about 3–10 ft) tall, often growing in dense colonies. The stems are round, swollen toward the lower end to a diameter of 2 cm (0.8 in.) or more, and gradually tapering at the top. The stem bases are white and succulent, the tops dark green with tough, pithy centres. The leaves, borne at the base of the stem, consist of two or three prominent brownish sheaths with or without short, poorly developed blades. The flower head or inflorescence is subtended by an erect, tapering, green bract 2–10 cm (0.8–4.0 in.)

Tule (*Scirpus acutus*).

—Nancy J. Turner

long, appearing as a continuation of the stem. The flowers are borne in numerous compact grey-brown spikelets which are clustered at the ends of a number of short branches spreading from a single point at the top of the stem. *Scirpus validus* Vahl, classed by some botanists as a separate species, is included in this book under the discussion of *S. acutus,* since native peoples consider them to be one and the same. Some botanists include both *S. acutus* and *S. validus* as subspecies of *S. lacustris* L.

HABITAT—Marshes and swampy ground at the edges of lakes and streams at lower elevations; sometimes growing in water 1 m (3 ft) or more deep.

DISTRIBUTION IN BRITISH COLUMBIA—Widespread in the Province in appropriate habitats, especially in the central and southern Interior, where it often forms extensive colonies around alkali lakes.

INDIAN USE—This plant was an important mat-making material for many of the Province's Indian groups, especially the Salishan peoples of the Coast and Interior. It was used to a lesser extent by the Nootka, Kwakiutl, Carrier, and Kootenay. The tall, round stems, pulpy but tough, were usually harvested at the peak of maturity in late summer and early fall, but the Okanagan gathered them in late November after they had already turned brown. If the plants are too young they are virtually impossible to pull up, but at the right stage they break off easily at the base with only a slight tug on the upper stem. If the water is not too deep where they are growing they can be cut with a knife. Care must be taken not to bend the stems during the harvesting process.

The stems were tied in large bundles and carried home, where they were spread out and dried in the sun. For making mats they were laid side by side alternating top and bottom and either sewn with a long wooden needle or twined together with a tough fibre such as stinging nettle or Indian hemp. Tule mats are light, with a good insulating capacity because of their pithy centre, and can be rolled easily longitudinally into a tight bundle. They served many purposes. The largest were used for the roofs and walls of temporary shelters, summer dwellings, and teepees, and as insulation for

Cowichan woman gathering tule stems. Photo by E. S. Curtis (*ca.* 1910), courtesy of the Provincial Archives of British Columbia.

the walls of winter houses. Medium sized mats were used as door covers, rugs, mattresses, and wind breaks, and for drying berries and cutting and drying meat and fish on. The smaller ones were used for covering windows, for sitting on at home or in the canoe, and for eating on. Extra softness for mattresses and sitting mats could be gained by piling two or more on top of each other.

The Okanagan made large bags suitable for storing dried roots, berries, and fish from tule woven with various other fibres, including silverberry bark, willow bark, or Indian hemp. They made a small ball, used in a ball and pin game with a red hawthorn spine for a pin, by folding a tule stem back and forth over itself and tying it. They also made headdresses for Indian doctors from tule. The Nootka made baskets, basket lids and, recently, handles for shopping-bags from it. The Vancouver Island Salish traded tule mats

"Cut-grass" (*Scirpus microcarpus*).

—Nancy J. Turner

to the Mainland Salish in exchange for mountain goat wool and wool blankets and in the 19th century exchanged them with the Nootka for halibut.

Two other species of *Scirpus* were used in British Columbia Indian technology: *S. americanus* Pers., a tall, triangular-stemmed species, and *S. microcarpus* Presl., commonly known as "cut-grass" because of its broad, razor-sharp leaves. Both, like *S. acutus,* grow in marshes. *Scirpus americanus* was used by the Nootka for weaving baskets and basket lids and handles. *Scirpus microcarpus* was utilized by the Okanagan for weaving berry and root baskets, although these could not withstand heavy use. The dried leaves were woven into buckskin dresses as trimming and were sometimes laid over and under food in steaming pits. The sharp-edged leaves were sometimes used as cutting implements, but were too fragile to be of much use.

Bear-grass

Xerophyllum tenax
(Pursh) Nutt.

(Lily Family)

(Liliaceae)

OTHER NAMES—Squaw-grass, deer-grass, basket-grass, pine lily, "American grass."

BOTANICAL DESCRIPTION—A large perennial herb with a short, stout rhizome and numerous tough, pointed, grass-like leaves usually 1.5–6 dm (0.5–2.0 ft) long, forming a dense clump at the base of an erect, leafy stem which often exceeds 1 m (about 3 ft) in height. The flowers are numerous, small, white and fragrant, in a dense, globe-shaped, pointed cluster.

HABITAT—Open woods and meadows usually at moderate to high elevations.

DISTRIBUTION IN BRITISH COLUMBIA—Restricted to the south-eastern corner of the Province, but occurring near sea level on the Olympic Peninsula in Washington and eastward to the Rocky Mountains.

INDIAN USE—The tough, minutely serrated leaves were used in Northwest Indian basketry, especially for fine imbrication, trimming and ornamentation. They were widely employed by the Nootka and Coast Salish of Vancouver Island, as well as by the Squamish, Sechelt, Thompson, Okanagan, Kootenay, and possibly as far north as the Chilcotin. Of these groups only the Kootenay had direct access to the plant, the others obtained it through trade from neighbouring Washington groups. The leaves were a common item of commerce at the Columbia Rapids, the centre of the Chinook salmon trade. Within the last few decades the price of bear-grass was set at about 50 cents for a small bundle of prepared leaves.

The leaves were harvested, cut to a uniform width by a gauged knife edge, then dried to a lustrous, creamy white colour. They

Bear-grass (*Xerophyllum tenax*).

—David Polster

were often used in their natural colour, but lend themselves well to dyeing, either with vegetable pigments or, unfortunately in the opinion of some, with aniline dyes. As early as 1902, Dr. C. F. Newcombe was prompted to remark, "The fatal facility with which *Xerophyllum* takes aniline dyes . . . and the demands of the average collector for gaudy shades has quite demoralized the colour sense of the Nootkans and their recent basket work is particularly discordant."

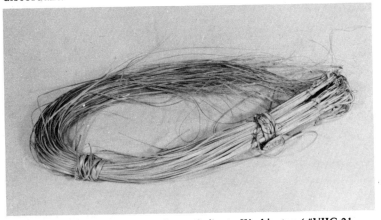

Bear-grass prepared for weaving at Quileute, Washington (#VIIG 21, National Museum of Man, Ottawa).
—Dorothy I. D. Kennedy

As well as for trimming and imbrication, the Nootka used the leaves for the weft in their finely twined baskets and also wove them into mats. The small baskets they sold to the Hudson's Bay Company for blue trading beads. They obtained their bear-grass leaves, which they called "American grass," from the Makah people of the Olympic Peninsula. The Kootenay used the leaves for hats. The Southern Okanagan and Sanpoil-Nespelem Okanagan of Washington, who obtained the leaves from the neighbouring Kalispel and Pend d'Oreille territories, used them to make designs on birch-bark baskets. Recently, corn husks were substituted when bear-grass was not obtainable.

Grasses

(Poaceae or Gramineae)

Grasses were used by British Columbia Indians in a general capacity for lining steaming pits, wiping fish, covering berries, spreading on floors, stringing clams, eulachon, and roots for drying, and as bedding. Coast Salish hunters lured deer by whistling through a blade of grass. The Kwakiutl used fresh green grass to colour abalone shells and spruce-root hats, and the Nootka made

Bunchgrass (*Agropyron spicatum*).

—Nancy J. Turner

a green dye for painting wood and basket materials by macerating grass, soaking it for a long time in hot water, and drying it into a cake, which was pulverized and mixed with oil.

A number of grasses, including pinegrass, ryegrass, sweetgrass, and reedgrass, were fairly important in Indian technologies and are discussed in detail. Several others were used in minor ways by British Columbia Indians and their neighbours. Bunchgrass [*Agropyron spicatum* (Pursh) Scribn. & Smith], a dominant species of the dry Interior, was used by the Okanagan as tinder for starting fires, and for stuffing moccasins in winter. Bunchgrass straws were inserted into newly pierced ears to keep the openings from sealing. The Lillooet dried Saskatoon berries on bunchgrass and sometimes used it to make a soapberry beater. It is also said to make excellent hay for livestock. The Sanpoil-Nespelem Okanagan wove mats from sloughgrass [*Beckmannia syzigachne* (Steud.) Fern.], using Indian hemp fibre to sew or weave the leaves together. Okanagan children played with the awned seeds of "speargrass" or "Coyote's needle" (*Stipa comata* Trin. & Rupr.), throwing them like darts. The Blackfoot of Alberta bound the awns of its relative, porcupine-grass (*Stipa spartea* Trin.) into a cylindrical bundle the size of a man's thumb and used this as a hairbrush. The Tlingit of Alaska used the split stems of several species of grasses to imbricate their fine spruce-root baskets. These include: bromegrass (*Bromus sitchensis* Trin.), bluejoint-grass [*Calamagrostis canadensis* (Michx.) Beauv. ssp. *langsdorfii* (Link) Hult.], woodreed [*Cinna latifolia* (Trevir.) Griseb.], tufted hairgrass [*Deschampsia caespitosa* (L.) Beauv.], and mannagrass [*Glyceria striata* (Lam.) A. S. Hitchc. (syn.—*Panicularia nervata* Kuntze)].

Pinegrass	*Calamagrostis rubescens* **Buckl.**
(Grass Family)	**(Poaceae or Gramineae)**

OTHER NAME—"timbergrass."

BOTANICAL DESCRIPTION—A perennial with creeping rhizomes and slender, tufted stems 6–10 dm (about 2–3 ft) tall and usually reddish at the base. The leaves are erect, flat or V-shaped, 2–4 mm (about 0.1–0.2 in.) wide, with smooth but slightly hairy sheaths. The flowers are borne, one per spikelet, in a narrow, greenish to purplish, somewhat irregular cluster 7–15 cm (3–6 in.) long.

HABITAT—A valuable range grass of open, dry sagebrush flats to moist montane forests.

DISTRIBUTION IN BRITISH COLUMBIA—An abundant species of the southern Interior from the Chilcotin to the lower Columbia Valley.

INDIAN USE—This species has been identified by several contemporary native people as "timbergrass," which was employed in a variety of ways by Interior Salish peoples. However, other identifications of "timbergrass" have been made, including a vegetatively similar species of *Poa* and a small woodland sedge, *Carex concinnoides* in Cyperaceae, which was discussed earlier.

Timbergrass leaves were gathered by the handful in the summer, cut and washed, and used in the preparation of "Indian icecream" a frothy confection made from soapberries (*Shepherdia*

A Thompson sock of dry "timbergrass" (#16/8615, American Museum of Natural History, New York).

—Dorothy I. D. Kennedy

canadensis L.). A bundle of grass was tied onto a stick to make a soapberry beater, or, as was the common practice among the Thompson and Shuswap, cooked, drained soapberries were spread on a "mat" of timbergrass leaves which were braided together at the ends and laid out on a rack. A small fire was lit under the rack to dry the berries, and they were stored away for winter with the grass still attached. For use, pieces of the dried cakes were soaked in water and mixed with the hands, the grass serving to whip the berries. The grass leaves were then skimmed off the top or discarded by the eater of the soapberry whip.

The Okanagan used timbergrass to line and cover berry baskets and in steaming pits to place over and under the food. The leaves were rubbed together to soften them and used to weave socks and moccasin insoles for keeping the feet warm in winter. They were also twisted into twine and were mixed with mud to chink log cabins (see also *Carex concinnoides*). Lillooet hunters washed their guns and traps in water using timbergrass as a sponge.

Ryegrass	*Elymus cinereus* Scribn. & Merr.
(Grass Family)	(Poaceae or Gramineae)

OTHER NAME—Giant wild-rye.

BOTANICAL DESCRIPTION—A robust perennial forming large clumps, with stout, erect stems often 1–2 m (about 3–6 ft) high. The leaf blades are firm, flat, strongly nerved, and up to 1.5 cm (0.6 in.) wide, the sheaths smooth to densely hairy. The flowers, 2–6 per spikelet, are borne in a dense, wheat-like spike 10–25 cm (4–10 in.) long. The spikelets are usually in clusters of three to five per node.

HABITAT—River banks, gulleys, dry washes, moist or dry slopes and plains, in sandy or gravelly soil.

DISTRIBUTION IN BRITISH COLUMBIA—A common species of the dry Interior, from the Thompson River to the Rocky Mountain Trench.

Ryegrass (*Elymus cinereus*).

—Nancy J. Turner

American dunegrass (*Elymus mollis*).

—Nancy J. Turner

INDIAN USE—The stiff, hollow fruiting stems were cut, "smoked" over a hot fire to prevent them from turning brown, then split and washed and used by Interior Salish peoples, especially the Thompson, to imbricate split cedar-root baskets. Some Okanagan groups made small, temporary arrows from the stems, notching them and fixing them with tips of mock-orange wood. These were used in games and for hunting certain small birds. Similarly, young Flathead boys fixed hawthorn points to the stems and used them as spears to inflict pain in preparation for warfare. The Okanagan used the leaves for lining steaming pits and food caches, covering the floors of winter houses and sweathouses if fir boughs were not available, and as bedding and horse fodder. They set a hollow ryegrass stem into the centre of a food cache before it was covered over to prevent the food from "sweating" and becoming affected with mildew. The Lillooet used the leaves, with Saskatoon branches, for lining steaming pits, and the Blackfoot used them for bedding. Another species of *Elymus, E. triticoides* Buckl., was reported by Dr. C. F. Newcombe and James Teit to be used in basketry by the Thompson and Lillooet and traded by them to the

A Haida spruce-root basket intertwined with stems of American dunegrass (#2-30955, R. H. Lowie Museum of Anthropology, Berkeley).

—Dorothy I. D. Kennedy

Stalo, Squamish and Sechelt on the Coast. However, *E. triticoides* does not actually grow in the Province; the species used must have been a related one, such as *E. glaucus* Buckl. or *E. canadensis* L. In any case, the stems were the part of the plant used, being cut, slit down one side, flattened and superimposed over the weave of baskets.

On the Coast, the leaves of another species, *E. mollis* Trin., commonly known as American dunegrass, or ricegrass, was used by the Vancouver Island Salish for weaving tumplines and pack-straps and for tucking into the ravels of reefnets to strengthen them. The Nootka sometimes used dunegrass leaves for weaving basket handles, and the Quinault of Washington wove tumplines from them and spread them out to dry salal berries on. The Haida split the stems in half, dyed them, and used them to twine and imbricate baskets. The Tlingit also used the stems as overlay for baskets, but only for coarse work or when the other species, mentioned earlier was not available.

Sweetgrass	***Hierochloë odorata***
	(L.) Beauv.
(Grass Family)	**(Poaceae or Gramineae)**

OTHER NAMES—Holy-grass, vanilla-grass, Seneca-grass.

BOTANICAL DESCRIPTION—A reddish-based perennial with slender, creeping rhizomes and leafy stems 3–5 dm (12–20 in.) tall. The leaf blades are usually 2–5 mm (about 0.1–0.2 in.) wide, and pointed. Those on the stem are fairly short, while those borne on vegetative shoots are up to 25 cm (10 in.) long. The flowers are small, 3 per spikelet, in an open pyramidal cluster. The leaves have a sweet, vanilla-like fragrance.

HABITAT—Moist meadows and slopes from moderate to sub-alpine elevations.

DISTRIBUTION IN BRITISH COLUMBIA—Widespread in the Province but seldom abundant.

INDIAN USE—The sweet, lingering fragrance of this grass is due to the presence of coumarin, a lactone glycoside which was form-

Sweetgrass (*Hierochloë odorata*).

erly used commercially as a flavouring agent. The grass was well-appreciated among North American Indians for its scent. The Seneca in the East wove fragrant baskets from the leaves. The Flathead of Montana and the Blackfoot of Alberta plaited bundles of the dried leaves into a thick, three-ply rope, which was used as a sachet in clothing or ignited at one end and burned as an incense, air and clothing freshner, and insect repellent. Alternately, the leaves were placed on a hot stove and allowed to smoke. Black-foot women often wore a plaited band of sweetgrass around their heads, braided it into clothing, or carried it around in a small buckskin bag as a perfume.

In British Columbia, the Kootenay used sweetgrass in a similar manner. They often purchased the thick braids of leaves from the Blackfoot and burned them like a punk to fumigate a house. They say that up in the mountains in some localities one can smell the fragrance of sweetgrass on the wind. The Thompson also used it, crumpled up in a bag as a sachet, tied in the hair or on neck and arm ornaments, or rubbed on the clothing, hair and skin.

Reed Canary-grass   *Phalaris arundinacea* L.

(Grass Family)   **(Poaceae or Gramineae)**

BOTANICAL DESCRIPTION—A tall, coarse perennial grass with creeping rootstocks and stout, erect stems up to 1.5 (4.5 ft) or more metres high. The leaves are flat and numerous, up to 12 mm (0.5 in.) wide. The flowers are borne in dense, compound clusters up to 18 cm (7 in.) long, narrow and erect at first, the branches spreading slightly at maturity.

HABITAT—Swamps, lake margins and roadside ditches, often in standing water. An important hay species.

DISTRIBUTION IN BRITISH COLUMBIA—Common throughout southern British Columbia, and north to the Peace River.

INDIAN USE—The Upper Stalo of the Fraser Valley, and prob-ably other Salish groups as well, used the stout, smooth stems for imbricating baskets. The stems were cut in May and early June while still pliable and green. They were cut into even lengths and

Reed canary-grass (*Phalaris arundinacea*).

—Nancy J. Turner

soaked in boiling water, then dried for several days in the sun to bleach them white. They were split, soaked, and used like the stems of the common reedgrass to superimpose white patterns on the weave of split-root baskets (Dr. Brent Galloway, pers. comm.). The Okanagan used this grass to make eating and food-drying mats, for weaving peaked hats for Indian doctors, and for binding fishing weirs.

Common Reedgrass	***Phragmites communis*** **(L.) Trin.**
(Grass Family)	**(Poaceae or Gramineae)**

BOTANICAL DESCRIPTION—A tall perennial with stout, creeping rhizomes and erect, leafy, conspicuously noded stems 2–4 m (6.5–13 ft) high. The leaf blades are 20–40 cm (8–16 in.) long, flat, and up to 5 cm (2 in.) wide, the sheaths smooth and loose, often twisting in the wind so that the leaves are all aligned in the same direction. The flowers are borne in dense, purplish to white, fuzzy, terminal clusters 15–35 cm (6–14 in.) long, resembling small heads of the ornamental pampas-grass.

HABITAT—Marshes, lake and river margins, and roadside ditches, often in standing water.

DISTRIBUTION IN BRITISH COLUMBIA—In appropriate habitats in the southern half of the Province, from Vancouver Island to the Okanagan; often forming dense colonies.

INDIAN USE—The smooth, glossy, hollow stems were used by the Thompson, Lillooet, Carrier, and probably other groups as well, as a material for imbricating split cedar-root baskets, much in the same way as ryegrass stems. James Teit considered them "one of the most commonly used basketry materials" (of the Thompson). They were split down one side, flattened, and dried. Usually their natural creamy white colour was maintained, but they were sometimes dyed yellow or some other colour. In creating basket decorations they were interspersed with natural red and dyed black strips of bitter cherry bark. The Thompson also cut and dyed lengths of the stems and used them with various seeds

Common reedgrass (*Phragmites communis*).

—Nancy J. Turner

and berries as decorative beads on necklaces and fringes of dresses. The Blackfoot of Alberta used the stems for arrow shafts and pipe stems. The Shuswap sometimes used *Phragmites* hay as bedding and for spreading around a camp to keep the dust down.

A Lillooet basket of split cedar root, imbricated with black and natural bitter cherry bark and (probably) the stems of common reedgrass (#57881, Field Museum of Natural History, Chicago).

—Dorothy I. D. Kennedy

Cat-tail   *Typha latifolia* L.

(Cat-tail Family)   (Typhaceae)

OTHER NAME—Sometimes called "bulrush" but this name is also applied to species of *Scirpus* in the sedge family (Cyperaceae).

BOTANICAL DESCRIPTION—A tall perennial with thick, white, fleshy rhizomes and long, sword-like leaves, greyish-green and mostly 1–2 cm (0.4–0.8 in.) wide, with a pithy inner tissue. The flowers are contained in a compact, brown spike, familiar to almost everyone as the "cat's tail." The pollen is produced on a thinner spike immediately above the brown portion. As the mature

Cat-tail (*Typha latifolia*).

—Robert D. Turner

fruits are released in late summer and fall, the "cat's tail" becomes a mass of whitish, cottony fuzz, which is gradually blown away in the wind.

HABITAT—Shallow marshes, swamps, and lake edges, often forming pure stands of several acres.

DISTRIBUTION IN BRITISH COLUMBIA—In appropriate habitats throughout the Province except on the central and northern Coast and the Queen Charlotte Islands; most common around ponds and lakes of the southern Interior.

INDIAN USE—The flat, spongy leaves were, along with tule stems, the most important mat-making material of the Salish peoples in the Province, and were used by other groups as well. The leaves were generally gathered in late summer, cut to even lengths, and dried in the sun. Mats were constructed by laying the leaves out side by side alternating top and bottom, and threading them together transversely at about ten-cm intervals, using a plant fibre such as nettle twine, or the lower edge of the cat-tail leaf itself. A long, thin needle of "ironwood" or some other hardwood was used in this procedure. It was poked through an entire row of leaves and the leaf tissue was firmly pressed around it with a "mat creaser," often of broad-leafed maple wood, to make an opening for the thread. Selvage pieces of braided cat-tail leaves were sewn at the edges and the ends were folded over and bound. These mats were up to two metres in length and of a width varying with the number of leaves used. They were used by the Coast and Interior Salish, Nootka, Kwakiutl, and Kootenay for insulating the walls of winter houses, for kneeling on in canoes, sitting on, drying berries on, covering doors and windows, and as saddle blankets, mattresses or mattress underlays, and carpeting. For extra softness, three or four mats would be piled on top of each other. The Nootka and Kwakiutl sometimes obtained cat-tail leaves or finished mats from the Salish through trade. It is generally maintained that these groups did not make cat-tail mats originally but learned the art from their Salish neighbours within the last century.

The leaves were also used by various groups to make twine, baskets, bags, capes, hats, and headdresses for Indian doctors.

Temporary summer house of cat-tail mats, Puget Sound, Washington. Photo by E. S. Curtis (*ca.* 1912), courtesy Provincial Archives of British Columbia, Victoria.

The Saanich, a Straits Salish group, split the leaves and spun them on the bare thigh to make storage baskets for camas bulbs and crabapples. They also made a baby's first cradle from bundles of cat-tail leaves tied together. The Lower Lillooet of the Pemberton area made a strong, 4-, 6-, or 8-strand rope by plaiting the leaves with the bark of red cedar roots. A tough, fine thread was made by the Squamish and other Coast Salish peoples by stripping off the thin edges of the whitish leaf bases with the fingernail, drying them, and rolling them together on the thigh.

The Straits Salish used charcoal from burned cat-tail leaves for tattooing, and the Kwakiutl mixed the charcoal from old burned cat-tail mats with water and dried herring spawn and used it as a paint for the insides of canoes to protect them from weathering.

Cat-tail seed fluff was used by the Interior Salish to stuff pillows and mattresses. One old-timer of the Lower Lillooet people remembers his mother collecting it by the gunnysackful for this pur-

pose.   The Okanagan and other groups used it for dressing wounds
and as baby diapers.   The baby's urine caused the fuzz to form
little balls, which were absorbent and easy to remove from the
cradle.   The Saanich sometimes spun the "cotton" with their dog
wool to make blankets.

Eel-grass and its relatives	*Zostera marina* and *Phyllospadix* species
(Eel-grass Family)	**(Zosteraceae—sometimes included in Najadaceae)**

OTHER NAMES—Sea-grass, ribbon-grass, basket-grass (applying to *Phyllospadix*).

BOTANICAL DESCRIPTION—Eel-grass and its relatives, *Phyllospadix scouleri* Hooker and *P. torreyi* Watson, are the only three
species of flowering plants on the British Columbia Coast which
are truely marine.   They are perennials, having long, flexible,
ribbon-like leaves and fleshy rhizomes.   Eel-grass has flat leaves,

Eel-grass (*Zostera marina*).

—Robert D. Turner

more than 32 mm (1.3 in.) wide, which are dull green. The two *Phyllospadix* species have bright emerald-green leaves, which are flat and usually under 1 m (3 ft) in length in *P. scouleri* and rounded and up to 3 m (10 ft) long in *P. torreyi*. The flowers are inconspicuous and pollinated under water with the aid of ocean currents. Two varieties of eel-grass occur: *Z. marina* var. *marina,* with leaves usually under 1.2 m (4 ft) long, and *Z. marina* var. *latifolia* Morong, with leaves up to 4 m (13 ft) long.

HABITAT—*Zostera* occurs in quiet, protected bays in mud or sand, while the *Phyllospadix* species usually occur on rocky, wave-swept shores.

DISTRIBUTION IN BRITISH COLUMBIA—All three species and both varieties of *Zostera marina* are found in appropriate habitats throughout the British Columbia Coast.

INDIAN USE—The Vancouver Island Salish and Kwakiutl used the damp leaves of eel-grass for generating steam in the board-bending process of making cedar-wood boxes and in other types of wood molding. The Haida, Nootka, and other Coastal groups

Sea-grass (*Phyllospadix scouleri*).

—Nancy J. Turner

153

occasionally collected herring spawn from the leaves of both eelgrass and *Phyllospadix*. The Nootka used *Phyllospadix* leaves, especially those of *P. scouleri,* to imbricate baskets. They could be sun-bleached to a bright white, or dyed black or any other colour required for a basket pattern. Quileute boys of Washington sometimes used bunches of the leaves as targets in arrow practice, but according to Erna Gunther, the Quileute never used *Phyllospadix* in basketry.

FLOWERING PLANTS (ANGIOSPERMAE)
DICOTYLEDONS

Vine Maple   *Acer circinatum* **Pursh**

(Maple Family)   **(Aceraceae)**

BOTANICAL DESCRIPTION—Small trees or tall, multi-stemmed shrubs, 3–10 m (about 10–30 ft) high with branches in opposite pairs. The bark is smooth and pale green to purplish-red. The leaves, 5–13 cm (2–5 in.) across, are palmately veined, having 7–9 deep, pointed lobes with saw-toothed margins. They are bright green, turning orange to scarlet in autumn. The flowers are 6–9 mm (about 0.2–0.4 in.) broad, with purplish sepals and white petals, borne in loose, few-flowered clusters. The fruits, in pairs, are smooth, with prominent, widely spreading wings.

HABITAT—Moist, shaded woods, from near sea level to sub-alpine elevations.

DISTRIBUTION IN BRITISH COLUMBIA—On the southern Coast from the Coast and Cascade Mountains westward, but with a few isolated reports further inland; rare on Vancouver Island.

INDIAN USE—The wood is hard, but limited in size and inclined to warp with time. The Clayoquot Nootka and the Quinault of Washington made large, open-work carrying baskets from vine maple splints, and the Quinault also used them for fish-traps. The Skagit of Washington made salmon tongs from the wood, the Katzie of the Fraser Valley used it for spoons, and the Squamish and Cowichan for knitting needles. The Squamish, Katzie, Lower Lillooet and Lower Thompson sometimes made bows from the

Vine maple (*Acer circinatum*).

—Robert D. Turner

long, straight branches. The last two groups also made snowshoes, slat armour vests, arrows, baby basket frames, implement handles, and sometimes dipnet frames from vine maple, as well as from Rocky Mountain maple. The Squamish also made dipnet frames from it. Additionally, the wood was sometimes used for fuel. The Quinault used the charcoal mixed with oil as a black paint.

Rocky Mountain Maple   *Acer glabrum* **Torr.**
(Maple Family)   **(Aceraceae)**

OTHER NAMES—Mountain maple, Douglas maple, sometimes mistakenly called vine maple.

BOTANICAL DESCRIPTION—A bushy shrub or small tree, 1–10 m (about 3–30 ft) tall, with opposite branches and smooth, greyish to reddish-purple bark. The leaves are usually 6–10 cm (2.4–4.0 in.) long and about the same across. They are palmately veined, with 3–5 sharp, coarsely toothed lobes. They turn a bright red-orange in the fall. The flowers, in small, loose clusters, are about 8 mm (0.3 in.) across and yellowish. The fruits are smooth and in pairs, with prominent wings usually with less than a 90-degree spread.

HABITAT—Coastal lowlands to dry, rocky slopes; usually in open locations.

DISTRIBUTION IN BRITISH COLUMBIA—From the east coast of Vancouver Island to the Rocky Mountains and northward to Alaska and Dawson Creek. Not found on the Queen Charlotte Islands. Abundant and widespread in the southern Interior.

INDIAN USE—Many Indian people, especially in the Interior, refer to this as "vine maple;" in areas where the range overlaps with that of the true vine maple, it is often difficult to tell which species is being referred to. The wood, which is tough and pliable, was employed in a variety of ways. The Thompson, Okanagan, Shuswap, Lillooet, and Carrier commonly used it to make snowshoe frames. In addition, the Thompson used it for the hoods of babies' cradles or baskets, for baby swings, and bows; the Okanagan for drum hoops, teepee pegs, and tongs; the Shuswap for digging sticks, fish traps, scoop net handles, spear prongs, and handles of spears and harpoons; the Lillooet for bows, arrows, and combs; and the Carrier for labrets. The Sekani used it for bows; the Chilcotin made throwing sticks from it; the Bella Coola made spoons and slat armour; the Niska made raven rattles, masks, and headdresses; and the Haida, who imported it from the Tsimshian on the Mainland, used it for carving grease dishes, soapberry spoons, sea otter

Rocky Mountain maple (*Acer glabrum*).

—Robert D. Turner

clubs, dipnet handles, gambling sticks and totem models. The Flathead of Montana made arrow shafts, pipe stems, and sweathouse frames from it. The green wood could be easily molded by first soaking it in water, then heating it over an open fire and bending it to the desired shape while still hot.

Shuswap snowshoes made of the wood of Rocky Mountain maple (#IID 2bab, National Museum of Man, Ottawa).

—Dorothy I. D. Kennedy

The wood was considered an excellent fuel. The Kootenay used it as the drill and hearth in making friction fires and the Bella Coola used it in the old days to fell red cedar trees. A long maple branch was bound around the base of a cedar and ignited. Once it caught fire it smouldered for a long time, eventually burning right through the tree. Near Bella Coola village, a cedar tree, partially burned through by this method many years ago, still stands with a maple branch embedded in the wood.

The fibrous bark of this maple was used by the Lillooet and Shuswap for making rope, for stringing roots, such as the corms of the yellow avalanche lily, together for drying, and, tied in a bundle to a stick, for whipping soapberries. The Niska on the Nass River wove mats from it, using black-dyed strands to make decorative patterns. The Blackfoot of Alberta made paint cases from folded sheets of the bark.

Broad-leafed Maple	*Acer macrophyllum* Pursh
(Maple Family)	(Aceraceae)

OTHER NAMES—Big-leaf maple, common maple.

BOTANICAL DESCRIPTION—A large, spreading tree up to 30 m (100 ft) high. The trunk and branches are often moss-covered. The bark is smooth and greenish or reddish when young, becoming rough and greyish with age. The leaves are the largest of any tree in the Province with a spread up to 30 cm (12 in.) or more. They are smooth-edged and palmately veined, with 5 prominent, pointed lobes, the larger ones with smaller lateral lobes. The flowers are small and yellow-green in long, hanging clusters. The fruits, in pairs, are covered with coarse, stiff hairs and have large, prominent wings spreading at an angle of less than 90 degrees.

HABITAT—Damp woods and slopes at lower elevations.

DISTRIBUTION IN BRITISH COLUMBIA — Along the southern Coast and sporadic northward to Alaska, west of the Coast and Cascade Mountains, and on Vancouver Island; not found on the Queen Charlotte Islands.

Broad-leafed maple (*Acer macrophyllum*).

—Robert D. Turner

INDIAN USE—The Coast Salish people and, to a lesser extent, the Nootka and Kwakiutl, used the wood for carving dishes, spoons, fishnet measures, fish lures, hairpins, combs, balls, cat-tail mat creasers, rattles, cedar-bark shredders, adze handles, and particularly spindle whorls and paddles. In fact, the name for this maple in a number of Coast Salish languages means "paddle-tree". The Lower Lillooet of the Pemberton area sometimes used the wood for pipe stems and snowshoe frames, although Rocky Mountain maple was usually preferred for the latter. This maple was considered an excellent fuel; it burns with a hot, smokeless flame. The

A Halkomelem spindle whorl of broad-leafed maple wood (#221179B, Smithsonian Institution, Washington, D.C.).

—Dorothy I. D. Kennedy

Squamish, and the Swinomish, Chehalis, and Quinault of Washington, used the decayed wood for smoking fish.

The inner bark was used by the Kwakiutl to weave open-work baskets, and by the Cowlitz in Washington for making ropes and tumplines. The Lower Thompson wove fans from it and sometimes tied a bundle on a stick, like Rocky Mountain maple bark, to make a small, mop-like beater for whipping soapberries.

The large leaves themselves were sometimes used in a bunch to whip soapberries, by groups such as the Straits Salish and Squamish. They were commonly spread under and over food in steaming pits, and were said to impart a pleasant flavour to cooking meat. They were also used to line berry baskets and even employed as small, makeshift berry containers. The Mainland Comox used them to line the pits in which salmon roe was buried to make "stink eggs", a great delicacy among some groups. The Squamish used them as "rags" to wipe the slime off freshly caught fish.

Cow Parsnip	***Heracleum lanatum* Michx.**
(Celery Family)	**(Apiaceae or Umbelliferae)**

OTHER NAMES—"Indian celery," "Indian rhubarb."

BOTANICAL DESCRIPTION—A robust, hollow-stemmed perennial, 1–3 m (3–10 ft) tall, from a stout taproot or root cluster. The leaves are broad and compound in three large segments (one terminal and two lateral), coarsely toothed and lobed. The flowers

Cow parsnip (*Heracleum lanatum*).

—Nancy J. Turner

162

are small, white, and numerous, arranged in large, flat-topped "umbrella-like" clusters, or umbels. The leafstalks are conspicuously winged at the base. The plants have a strong, pungent odour, especially when mature.

HABITAT—Moist, open areas, roadsides, and meadows, from sea level to above the treeline in the mountains; often in large patches.

DISTRIBUTION IN BRITISH COLUMBIA—General throughout the Province.

INDIAN USE—The large leaves were used by the Shuswap for covering berry baskets and by the Carrier for drying Saskatoon berries on. The Shuswap and the Flathead of Montana used the dried hollow stems to make elk and moose whistles, while the Haida used them as molds for making spruce gum "dice," employed in a game. The Blackfoot of Alberta made children's flutes, drinking straws, and toy blowguns from them. The large "umbrella-spoked" flower heads were entwined with seaweed by girls of the Makah and Quileute groups in Washington to make play baskets for holding shells and small objects. The Shuswap boiled the entire plant in water to make a washing solution for eliminating fleas from clothing.

Chocolate Tips

(Celery Family)

Lomatium dissectum
(Nutt.) Math. & Const.

(Apiaceae or Umbelliferae)

BOTANICAL DESCRIPTION—A robust, multi-stemmed perennial, often 1 m (over 3 ft) or more high, from a large woody taproot. The leaves are large, especially the basal ones, and finely dissected into numerous small segments. The flowers are small and purple, clustered in large, flat-topped umbels. The fruits are elliptic and narrowly winged. (Also known as *Leptotaenia dissecta* Nutt. and *Ferula dissecta* Gray.)

HABITAT—Dry, rocky slopes, from sea level to moderate elevations in the mountains.

163

Chocolate tips (*Lomatium dissectum*).

—Nancy J. Turner

DISTRIBUTIONS IN BRITISH COLUMBIA—Sporadic in the southern part of the Province, on both sides of the Cascades. Common at Botanie Valley near Lytton, and in parts of the Okanagan Valley.

INDIAN USE—The tops and roots are considered poisonous by the Okanagan, although the new shoots were formerly eaten in the spring before they emerged from the ground. Other Interior Salish groups actually ate the young roots as well. The Okanagan used the roots as a fish poison and insecticide. They pounded the roots and steeped them in water overnight to make a milky-coloured infusion. This liquid was then poured into the creek, causing the fish to float to the surface, where women and children could gather them and clean them. The poison lost its effectiveness once it had flowed downstream about half a mile. Fish killed in this way were not harmful to eat as long as they were consumed soon afterward. The same solution was poured over horses and cattle to rid them of lice and other insect pests. Rubbing the animals with the leaves and stems of the plant achieved the same results.

Indian Consumption Plant   *Lomatium nudicaule*
                                      (Pursh) Coult. & Rose

(Celery Family)   **(Apiaceae or Umbelliferae)**

OTHER NAME—"Wild celery."

BOTANICAL DESCRIPTION—A herbaceous perennial from a stout taproot, mostly 2–6 dm (8–24 in.) high, with stems solitary or clustered. The leaves are thick, bluish-green, and compound, divided into 3–30 oval-shaped leaflets, which may or may not be toothed at the tips. The flowers are light yellow, small, and numerous, in loose, "umbrella-like" clusters, with rays of varying lengths. The fruits are oblong or ellipse-shaped, winged, and flattened.

HABITAT—Dry, open slopes, moist meadows, and sparsely wooded areas from sea level to moderate elevations in the mountains.

Indian consumption plant (*Lomatium nudicaule*).

—Nancy J. Turner

DISTRIBUTION IN BRITISH COLUMBIA—In the southern part of the Province, both west and east of the Cascade Range; common on Vancouver Island and the Gulf Islands, as well as in many Interior locations.

INDIAN USE—The seeds, which are spicy and aromatic, were widely used as a fumigant and house deodorant. The Saanich, Squamish, Lower Lillooet, and Shuswap all used them for this purpose. The Saanich and Squamish placed them on a hot stove, allowing the smoke to penetrate the air. The Saanich also used them as a flavouring for meat and fish, and burned them in the hut where salmon was drying, to prevent supernatural contamination. The Lower Lillooet burned them in an open fire, not only as a fumigant but as a mosquito repellent. The Shuswap placed the seeds under the mattress of a baby's basket as a scent, and also under the pillow of an older person to disinfect and deodorize the bed; it was said to act like baby powder. The leaves of a related species, the "wild carrot" [*L. macrocarpum* (Nutt.) Coult. & Rose], were used by the Thompson as a scent, and as padding on child carriers to make the child sleep well. The Flathead of Montana used yet another *Lomatium* species [*L. triternatum* (Pursh) Coult. & Rose], in perfume bags as a scent, and the Blackfoot of Alberta stuffed the seeds of this species into animal pelts during the tanning process.

Indian Hemp and
Spreading Dogbane
(Dogbane Family)

Apocynum cannabinum **L.**
and *A. androsaemifolium* **L.**
(Apocynaceae)

BOTANICAL DESCRIPTION—Indian hemp is an erect, bushy perennial herb 3–10 dm (12–40 in.) tall, with smooth, often reddish stems and many opposite, finely pointed, elliptic to lance-shaped leaves, 5–11 cm (about 2–4 in.) long. The leaves are yellowish-green, turning golden-yellow in the fall. A milky latex exudes from the stems when broken. The flowers, which bloom in summer, are small, tubular, and whitish, in axillary or terminal clusters. The fruits, in pairs, are long, 12–18 cm (5–7 in.), and

Indian hemp (*Apocynum cannabinum*).

—Robert D. Turner

Spreading dogbane (*Apocynum androsaemifolium*).

—Nancy J. Turner

slender, splitting open along one side when ripe to reveal numerous small, brown seeds, each with a long tuft of cottony hairs to aid in dispersal. Spreading dogbane is similar to Indian hemp, but with shorter stems, drooping, oval-shaped leaves, and fragrant, showy pink flowers. The two species occasionally hybridize where their ranges overlap.

HABITAT—Both plants grow in open, dry areas, along road-sides and in clearings, often forming dense patches.

DISTRIBUTION IN BRITISH COLUMBIA—Indian hemp is common in the valleys and lower slopes of the southern Interior, while spreading dogbane grows from sea level to moderate elevations in the mountains in many locations throughout the Province except on the Queen Charlotte Islands.

INDIAN USE—Indian hemp was without doubt the most important source of plant fibre for native peoples in the southern Interior. Spreading dogbane was also used when Indian hemp was not available, but being shorter and bushier was at best a poor sub-stitute. A description of the procedures for preparing Indian hemp fibre, as used by the Okanagan, is as follows: The stems were harvested in September or October just as the leaves were turning yellow. Damp areas were said to produce the tallest, thickest plants. The branches and leaves were removed and the stems were flattened by pulling them over a pole tied to a tree. They were then split open from bottom to top with a knife or sharp stick. The outer skin or "bark" was peeled off by hand and the inner fibrous parts were bundled together and hung by the tops to dry in the wind. When dry, the stems became brittle and the pithy middle tissue was separated from the fibre by pounding the flattened pieces with a stick or twisting them with the hands. The fibres were then formed into twine by rolling them with dampened hands on the bare thigh or on a piece of buckskin draped over the leg, with one end of the fibre being held to maintain the tension.

To join the fibre segments together into a continuous length of twine, the thick end of one piece and the thin end of another were each split about one half the length of the stem and these were spliced together as an interlocking "V", then rolled together until they were intertwined. The splicing process could continue almost indefinitely; some of the balls of twine produced were as large as basketballs. An average plant yields about two and a half feet of fibre, but nearly half of this is lost in splicing. A finer twine could be produced by splitting the stems in two along the entire length and splicing and rolling the halves together in the same manner as the whole pieces. Strong ropes could be made by twisting or plaiting two or more strands of twine together. A good, several-ply Indian hemp rope is said to have the equivalent strength of a modern rope of several hundred pounds test weight. Even the thinnest of threads is difficult to break with the hands. When stored properly, Indian hemp fibre will keep for many years without deteriorating. Its natural colour is a very light tan, almost white.

The Okanagan and other Interior groups, including the Thompson, Lillooet, Shuswap, and Kootenay, used Indian hemp twine for fishing lines and nets—because it keeps its strength under water

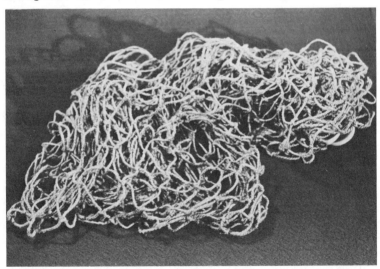

An Interior Salish Indian hemp fishing net (#1201, Ethnology Division, British Columbia Provincial Museum, Victoria).

—Robert D. Turner

and will not shrink—and for deer nets, slings, bowstrings, bridle ropes, nooses for game birds, hide stretchers, for binding implements, for sewing moccasins, clothing, baskets, birch-bark canoes, and cat-tail mats, and for weaving tumplines, garments, baby bedding, and bags. It was often woven with other plant fibres, such as silverberry, willow, sagebrush, and tule, and in making garments it was sometimes spun with deer hair. Among the Lillooet, Indian hemp fishing lines were treated with a mixture of lodgepole pine pitch and black bear grease to prevent them from kinking. They could be coloured with green leaves or alder bark dye to make them less conspicuous to fish. The loose fibre was used in some areas as a tinder for starting fires.

Indian hemp fibre from the Interior Salish (#1217, Ethnology Division, British Columbia Provincial Museum, Victoria).

—Robert D. Turner

Raw or spun, the fibre was a common trading product, not only amongst the various Indian groups of the southern Interior, but between them and the Coastal peoples, as far west as Vancouver Island. In the early days of contact with the white man, a large bundle of prepared twine was worth as much as a horse in the Okanagan area. On the Coast, the twine was a prized material for net-making, superior even to stinging nettle twine. A certain amount of Indian hemp fibre was undoubtedly traded to the Carrier and other Athapaskan peoples to the north, but for the most part they had to content themselves with spreading dogbane fibre, which was prepared by a similar process. The Bella Coola, as well as using dogbane as a source of fibre, used the bushy plants to fan the face on hot summer days.

Devil's-club

Oplopanax horridum (J. E. Smith) Miq.

(Ginseng Family)

(Araliaceae)

BOTANICAL DESCRIPTION—A straggly deciduous shrub, 1– 3 m (about 3–10 ft) high having greyish-brown bark and soft wood with a distinctive sweetish odour. The stems, leaf petioles, and leaf veins are covered with numerous thin, sharp spines which can inflict painful wounds to those who touch them. The leaves are large and maple-leaf shaped, with 7–9 shallow, pointed lobes and toothed margins. In good sites they may grow to 3 dm (1 ft) or more across. The flowers are small and whitish, in compact heads arranged in pyramidal, terminal clusters. The fruits are bright red, flattened, spiny berries.

Devil's club (*Oplopanax horridum*).

—Robert D. Turner

172

HABITAT—Moist, shady coniferous wood, often along stream banks and seepage faces in rich, black soil; occurs from sea level to subalpine elevations.

DISTRIBUTION IN BRITISH COLUMBIA—Common along the Coast from Vancouver Island to Alaska, and recurring in the Interior wet belt and as far north as the Fort Nelson River.

INDIAN USE—The stems were used by the Haida to hook black cod and octopus. The Klallam of Washington and some Vancouver Island Nootka groups peeled the sticks and cut them into small pieces for use as fish lures. The Manhousat Nootka actually carved them to resemble small fish. Attached to fishing lines near the hook, they would spin to the surface underwater. The fish, attracted by the moving object, would unwittingly become ensnared on the hook. The Straits Salish groups—including the Saanich, Songhish, and Lummi—and the Squamish, formerly mixed devil's club charcoal with bear grease to make a black face paint for ceremonial occasions. Some people even inserted it under the skin as a bluish-coloured tattoo. Erna Gunther in *The Ethnobotany of Western Washington* (1945) reports that the Lummi were still using devil's-club charcoal for face paint in the 1940's but that they were mixing it with vaseline instead of grease.

Showy Milkweed	*Asclepias speciosa* **Torr.**
(Milkweed Family)	**(Asclepiadaceae)**

BOTANICAL DESCRIPTION—A usually bushy herbaceous perennial, 4–12 dm (1.3–4.0 ft) tall. The leaves are opposite, smooth-edged, lance-shaped to oval, up to 20 cm (8 in.) long and about half as wide, with conspicuous transverse veins. The stems and leaves are covered with soft, woolly hairs which give the plants a greyish cast. The stems when broken exude a white, sticky latex, giving the plant its common name. The flowers are light to dark pink, numerous and showy, in one or more rounded, umbrella-shaped clusters. The fruits are conspicuous, light green, broadly spindle-shaped capsules, up to 10 cm (4 in.) or more long, and covered with soft, recurved spines. They split open along one side

Showy milkweed (*Asclepias speciosa*).

—Robert D. Turner

when ripe to reveal numerous flat, brown seeds, each with a long tuft of white, silky hairs which aid in dispersal.

HABITAT—Dry roadsides to moist meadows and stream banks in sandy to loamy soil.

DISTRIBUTION IN BRITISH COLUMBIA—East of the Cascade Mountains throughout the southern Interior.

INDIAN USE—The Thompson and other Interior Salish groups sometimes used the stem fibre as a substitute for Indian hemp fibre to make twine for binding and tying. It was, however, considered of inferior quality and was employed only when Indian hemp was not available. The stems were harvested in the fall, like those of Indian hemp, and were prepared similarly. Some Okanagan people call milkweed "Coyote's Indian hemp" as a nickname, alluding to a mythical event in which Coyote transformed some milkweed plants into Indian hemp by urinating on them.

Pasture Wormwood and its relatives

Artemisia frigida **Willd.,**
A. dracunculus **L. and**
A. ludoviciana **Nutt.**

(Aster or Composite Family) **(Asteraceae or Compositae)**

OTHER NAMES—These and other species of *Artemisia* are commonly called wormwood or sagebrush; *A. dracunculus* is called dragon sagewort or wild tarragon, and *A. ludoviciana* is called mugweed or cudweed sagewort.

BOTANICAL DESCRIPTION—*Artemisia frigida* is a low, mat-forming aromatic perennial with a branching woody crown. The flowering stems are 1–4 dm (4–16 in.) high. The leaves are small and numerous, clustered at the base and spaced along the stems. They are finely dissected into many narrow segments. The minute, composite flowers are compacted in small, yellowish disks which are borne in elongated, irregular, terminal clusters. The stems, leaves, and flower heads are covered with a dense mat of white, silky hairs, giving the entire plant a silvery appearance. *Artemisia dracunculus* is also a perennial, with several tall stems ascending

Pasture wormwood (*Artemisia frigida*).

—Nancy J. Turner

from a stout rhizome. It can be strongly aromatic or nearly odourless, smooth or slightly hairy, but never densely woolly. The leaves are long and slender, entire or sometimes deeply cleft, the lower ones soon drooping. The flower heads are minute and green, in loose, compound, terminal clusters. *Artemisia ludoviciana* is a tall, strongly aromatic perennial with silver-woolly leaves and stems. The leaves are lance-shaped and, in var. *latiloba* Nutt., sharply lobed. The flower heads are small, in compact, elongated, terminal clusters.

HABITAT—All three species grow in dry, open places in sandy or gravelly soil.

DISTRIBUTION IN BRITISH COLUMBIA—All are found in dry locations east of the Coast and Cascade Mountains. The range of *A. frigida* extends north into the Peace River country, while the other two are confined to the southern half of the Province.

INDIAN USE—These three wormwoods were all valued for their pungent, aromatic fragrance, which acts as an effective insect repellent. Branches of *A. frigida* and *A. dracunculus* were burned by the Okanagan, Shuswap and Kootenay, and the Blackfoot of Alberta, as a smudge to drive away mosquitoes and other biting insects. They could also be placed under pillows and mattresses to get rid of bedbugs, fleas, and lice. The Okanagan, Shuswap and Blackfoot employed *A. ludoviciana* similarly. Other aromatic species of *Artemisia* were also used in areas where they occurred.

Because of its pleasant smell, the Shuswap used *A. frigida,* mixed with Douglas-fir boughs, to cover the floor of a sweathouse. The Thompson often used it for smoking hides, since it burns with a thick, heavy smoke. *A. dracunculus* was used by the Shuswap as matting to sit on and by the Okanagan to pad baby boards, cradles, and diapers. It was said to keep the baby cool on a hot day and had the added advantage of healing diaper rash and rawness of the skin. The Okanagan also used the branches with the leaves still attached to make salmon spreaders for drying and storing salmon; the strong smell repelled flies and kept them from laying eggs in the flesh. The Flathead of Montana used the foliage of *A. ludoviciana* along with Douglas-fir boughs in their sweathouses as an

Dragon sagewort (*Artemisia dracunculus*).

—Nancy J. Turner

incense, and rubbed hides with it before they were soaked to prevent them from going sour. The Blackfoot used *A. frigida* and *A. ludoviciana* as a deodorant for saddles, pillows, hide bags, quivers, and moccasins, and also as toilet paper and for cleaning paint applicators. They rubbed hides with an infusion of the stems and roots of *A. frigida* or the roots of *A. campestris* L. as a curing agent.

Big Sagebrush   *Artemisia tridentata* Nutt.
(Aster or Composite Family)   (Asteraceae or Compositae)

OTHER NAME—Common sagebrush.

BOTANICAL DESCRIPTION—An erect, branching shrub up to 2 m (6.5 ft) tall, with grey, shredding bark and a strong aromatic odour. The leaves and young twigs are covered with a dense mat of fine, silvery hairs, giving the plants a soft, pale-grey appearance. The leaves, 1–4 cm (0.4–1.6 in.) long, are mostly wedge-shaped with three rounded terminal teeth. They remain on the bushes during the winter. Flowering time is late summer and fall. The flower heads are minute and greenish-grey in large, branching, terminal clusters.

HABITAT—Dry, open plains and woods, extending to subalpine elevations in some locations.

DISTRIBUTION IN BRITISH COLUMBIA — Common throughout the dry southern Interior; plentiful on overgrazed sites, since it is unpalatable to livestock.

INDIAN USE—Like the other species of *Artemisia* mentioned, this one was valued by Interior peoples for its strong, aromatic scent. The Shuswap and other groups placed the branches on a hot stove to fumigate a house. They also boiled the foliage and used the solution for washing walls and floors, as a disinfectant and insect repellent. The Lillooet used the leaves as a deodorizer when handling corpses.

The stringy, shredding bark of both stems and, according to one source, roots was pulled off in long strips and used by all the

Big sagebrush (*Artemisia tridentata*).

—Nancy J. Turner

Thompson shoes of big sagebrush bark (#16/9117a, American Museum of Natural History, New York).

—Dorothy I. D. Kennedy

Interior Salish groups to weave mats, bags, baskets, quiver cases, saddle blankets, dresses, skirts, aprons, breechclouts, ponchos, capes, and even shoes. However, it is said that only poor people, who did not have access to skins or other material, used sagebrush bark to make clothing. Often the bark was woven with other fibres such as willow bark, red cedar bark, silverberry bark, or Indian hemp. The Okanagan used the bark for stuffing pillows, especially in a child's cradle. The Thompson made quiver cases by binding the twigs together in a cylinder and sewing a piece of hide over the end. The Lillooet used the roots, hollowed out, to make temporary pipes.

The wood was often used as a fuel, for cooking and smoking hides; it burns easily and is plentiful in the dry Interior where there are few trees. The shredded bark made excellent tinder and was commonly used, as red cedar bark was on the Coast, for making a "slow match" to carry on journeys. The Lillooet macerated the old dry bark, formed it into a tight ball and bound it with birch-

A Thompson basket of twisted, sagebrush bark twined with silverberry bark; the hoop is of sandbar willow (#II-C-244, National Museum of Man, Ottawa).

—Dorothy I. D. Kennedy

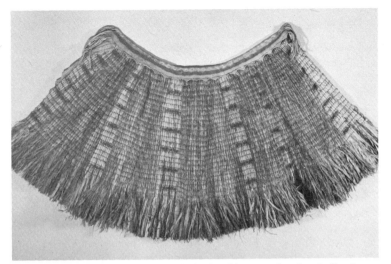

A Thompson cape of sagebrush bark with some bands of silverberry bark, twined with Indian hemp (#85695, Field Museum of Natural History, Chicago).

—Dorothy I. D. Kennedy

bark, while the Okanagan twisted it into a rope two or three feet long. In either case, when ignited it would smoulder for a long time and could be transported easily from place to place and used at any time to kindle a fire.

Balsamroot
Balsamorhiza sagittata (Pursh) Nutt.

(Aster or Composite Family)   **(Asteraceae or Compositae)**

OTHER NAMES—Spring sunflower, "wild sunflower."

BOTANICAL DESCRIPTION—A perennial 30 to 50 cm (12–18 in.) high, from a thick, deep-seated taproot, with numerous large, clustered, long-stemmed, arrow-head shaped leaves, which have a grey or silvery cast from a thick covering of fine white hairs. The flower heads, usually many per plant, are borne on individual stems, and are bright yellow, resembling small sunflowers, with about 25 petal-like ray flowers per head. The fruits, which shake loose easily from the old dried flower heads, are like miniature sunflower seeds. Blooming season is from April to July, at which time these plants provide a striking display of colour on the hillsides and valleys of the southern Interior.

HABITAT—Open, dry hillsides and flats, from lowlands to moderate elevations in the mountains; particularly prevalent in overgrazed areas.

DISTRIBUTION IN BRITISH COLUMBIA—Widespread throughout the southern Interior of the Province; showy and abundant.

INDIAN USE—The Okanagan stuffed the large hairy leaves in their moccasins in the winter to keep the feet warm. (They also used "timbergrass" and deer hair for this purpose.) Young Okanagan boys training to acquire supernatural power would wrap the leaves around their feet, pinning them on with bunchgrass stems, and walk on them to see how far they could get without tearing

Balsamroot (*Balsamorhiza sagittata*).

—Robert D. Turner

184

them. This exercise was to prepare them for walking in the woods silently and carefully with moccasins. It was said that certain gifted boys could even jog with the leaves on their feet.

Rabbitbrush

Chrysothamnus nauseosus
(Pall.) Britt.

(Aster or Composite Family)   **(Asteraceae or Compositae)**

BOTANICAL DESCRIPTION—A bushy shrub, usually about 1 m (3 ft) tall, with a strong, pungent odour. The branches are thin and erect. The twigs and leaves are covered with fine whitish hairs which give the plant a silvery cast. The leaves are 2–7 cm (0.8–2.8 in.) long, narrow and pointed, spreading outward and upward from the stems. The flower heads are bright yellow and numerous, in dense, showy, flat-topped, terminal clusters. This is a highly variable species, with numerous regional and ecological phases.

Rabbitbrush (*Chrysothamnus nauseosus*).

—Steve Cannings

185

HABITAT—Dry, open places in valleys, plains, and hillsides to moderate elevations in the mountains.

DISTRIBUTION IN BRITISH COLUMBIA—In appropriate habitats throughout the southern Interior.

INDIAN USE—Most native people consider this to be a type of sagebrush, or closely related to it. The Okanagan sometimes used the pungent smelling branches for smoking hides. The Sanpoil-Nespelem Okanagan of Washington pulverized the leaves and twigs and rubbed them on horses to protect them from horseflies and gnats. The Shuswap employed the cottony fruiting heads for stuffing pillows and mattresses.

| Vanilla-leaf | *Achlys triphylla* (Smith) DC. |
| (Barberry Family) | (Berberidaceae) |

OTHER NAMES—Sweet-after-death, May leaves, deer-foot.

BOTANICAL DESCRIPTION—A rhizomatous perennial herb, usually 15 cm (6 in.) or more high, with a single, long-stemmed, light green leaf ascending from ground level. It is 3-foliate, with one terminal leaflet and two lateral ones, all more or less lobed or wavy-edged. The flowers are small and white, lacking petals or sepals. They are borne in a compact, bottlebrush-like cluster at the end of a thin, wiry stem arising from the ground at the same point as the leaf. The fruits are small, rounded, and greenish or reddish-purple.

HABITAT—Moist, shaded woods, often growing in dense patches.

DISTRIBUTION IN BRITISH COLUMBIA—Along the southern Coastal region, from the east slopes of the Cascade Mountains westward; common on southeastern Vancouver Island.

INDIAN USE—The leaves when dried have a faint vanilla-like odour, as implied by the common name. They were used by the Saanich of Vancouver Island, the Thompson, and probably other groups on the southern Coast, as an insect repellent. The Saanich dried the leaves and hung them in bunches in houses to keep flies

Vanilla-leaf (*Achlys triphylla*).

—Nancy J. Turner

and mosquitoes away. The Thompson boiled the leaves and used the solution to bathe the skin of people infected with lice. It was also employed for washing bedding, furniture, and floors to eliminate bedbugs and other insect pests, and was said to be effective against skin parasites on sheep.

Oregon Grape **_Berberis aquifolium_
Pursh and _B. nervosa_ Pursh**

(Barberry Family) **(Berberidaceae)**

OTHER NAMES—Barberry, mahonia; *B. aquifolium* is sometimes called tall Oregon grape or tall mahonia.

BOTANICAL DESCRIPTION—Low shrubs with leathery, holly-like, compound leaves, elongated clusters of bright yellow flowers, and long clusters of round, deep-blue berries having a greyish waxy coating. The bark is light yellow-grey outside and bright yellow

Oregon Grape (*Berberis aquifolium*).

—Robert D. Turner

inside. *Berberis aquifolium* is taller than *B. nervosa* and has 5 to 7 leaflets per leaf, whereas *B. nervosa* has usually 9 to 15 leaflets per leaf.

HABITAT—*Berberis aquifolium* grows in open, dry, rocky areas, while *B. nervosa* prefers light to shaded coniferous forest.

DISTRIBUTION IN BRITISH COLUMBIA—*Berberis aquifolium* occurs throughout the southern part of the Province. *Berberis nervosa* is confined to the southern Coastal forests west of the Cascade Mountains. Neither is found on the Queen Charlotte Islands.

INDIAN USE—The inner bark of the stems and roots of both species contains a bright yellow pigment which can be extracted simply by boiling in water. Several Coastal Indian groups, including Cowichan, Straits Salish, Nootka, and the Chehalis, Skagit, and Snohomish of Washington, used both *Berberis aquifolium* and *B. nervosa* for dyeing basket materials, while the Thompson and Okanagan used *B. aquifolium,* the only one available in their area.

The sticks and roots were shredded and a generous handful was boiled in about a quart of water. The material to be dyed was then steeped in the solution. Bear-grass was often coloured by this method when used in basketry. Within the last few decades the Upper Skagit were using Oregon grape to dye rags for making braided rugs.

The Okanagan dyed porcupine quills with Oregon grape, and made a thick concentrated paint from it by boiling the dye solution until the water had evaporated, leaving a yellow powdery substance. This was mixed with ochre paint or cottonwood bud resin. The colour of the paint was often intensified by boiling wolf lichen along with the Oregon grape.

Some Vancouver Island Coast Salish groups used an extract of Oregon grape roots as a detergent lotion for washing the hands.

**Red Alder and
its relatives**

Alnus rubra **Bong.,** *A. incana*
(L.) Moench, and *A.
sinuata* **(Regel) Rydb.**

(Birch Family)

(Betulaceae)

OTHER NAMES—Red alder is also called Oregon alder; *A. incana* is called mountain alder, white alder, or thinleaf alder; *A. sinuata* is called Sitka alder, slide alder, green alder, or mountain alder.

BOTANICAL DESCRIPTION—Red alder is a fast-growing, straight-trunked, deciduous tree up to 25 m (about 80 ft) tall, with trunks up to 8 dm (30 in.) in diameter. The bark when young is smooth and greenish, becoming coarse and grey or whitish with age. The bark and wood tend to turn deep red or orange when exposed to moist air. The leaves are bright green, lighter beneath, oval-shaped, pointed, and coarsely toothed. The male flowers are borne in long, hanging, clustered catkins, which release large clouds of pollen when they ripen in early spring. The female flowers are borne in short, clustered, egg-shaped "cones," green and resinous when immature, brown and woody when ripe. The fruits or nutlets are small, flat, and slightly winged laterally.

The other species are similar to red alder, but generally lower, more bushy and shrub-like, with more finely-toothed, often doubly serrated, leaves. *Alnus incana* has nonwinged nutlets and blunt winter buds, while *A. sinuata* has broadly winged nutlets and sharply acute winter buds. [A common synonym for *A. incana* is *A. tenuifolia* Nutt.; *A. sinuata* is sometimes called *A. sitchensis* (Regel) Sarg.]

HABITAT—All three species grow in cool, moist woods, along stream banks and swamp edges. Red alder is a common "pioneer" species of recently logged areas; *A. sinuata* often forms dense patches on slide areas and avalanche runs in the mountains.

DISTRIBUTION IN BRITISH COLUMBIA—Red alder is common west of the Coast and Cascade Mountains along the entire Coast, and also occurs sporadically in the southern and central Interior. *A. incana* is found throughout the Interior east of the Coast

190

Red alder (*Alnus rubra*).

—Nancy J. Turner

Mountains, except in the far northeastern corner of the Province, while *A. sinuata* grows in appropriate habitats throughout.

INDIAN USE—Alders were extensively utilized by British Columbia Indians, for dyeing, for carving, and for fuel. As a source of dye they are known to native peoples across the continent. In the Province virtually every Indian group used alder in this capacity. Red alder was used along the Coast and in some areas of the Interior where it could be found; otherwise mountain alder or occasionally Sitka alder was used. Both wood and bark were employed. Colours ranging from almost black to dark brown to russet to bright orange-red were obtained by varying the preparation techniques. Basket materials, cedar bark, ropes, fishing nets and lines, wooden articles, mountain goat wool, feathers, porcupine quills, human hair, and buckskin were all dyed with alder. It was even used for tattooing.

The simplest method of preparing alder dye was to boil the bark and/or wood in a small quantity of water, and then to steep the material to be coloured in the solution. This procedure usually yielded a reddish-brown dye, suitable for fishing nets and basket materials. It had the effect of making nets and lines invisible to fish under water. The Haida, Nootka, and Kwakiutl produced a brighter red for cedar bark by chewing the alder bark, spitting the saliva into a container, and bringing it to a boil by adding red hot rocks.

The Kwakiutl, Tlingit, and Bella Coola often used urine as a mordant to obtain a bright red dye. The Tlingit carved vessels out of red alder trunks and filled them with children's urine, allowing it to stand for a time until it absorbed the red colouring from the alder wood, then dipped the material to be dyed into the solution. The Bella Coola used the following procedure: In summer they used scrapings from the inner bark, in winter large pieces of the bark with the wood attached. They placed water into a vessel, then added urine and alder bark. Using red hot rocks they heated this mixture gradually to the boiling point, stirring it occasionally. When it boiled, some of the bark was taken out and more added. This process was continued until the solution was a deep red. It was allowed to stand for a few minutes, then the cedar bark or other material to be dyed was put in, gently worked until saturated, and finally hung up to dry. Several pieces of cedar bark could be dyed in the same solution provided more bark and stones were added at intervals to maintain the proper strength and temperature. T. F. McIlwraith, who recorded this procedure in his book, *The Bella Coola Indians* (1948), stated that it was still being followed in the 1940's and that even at that time hot rocks were used to heat the solution, because it was believed that heating on a stove would produce inferior results.

The Saanich, a Straits Salish group, mixed red alder bark with cedar bark and Indian paint fungus, burned them to a powder, and inserted this under the skin with a needle, as a tattoo. They also put the bark in steaming pits to colour their camas bulbs pink. The Haida used the charcoal from the wood for tattooing and put about half a cup of the bark in their wash water as a bleach substitute. Several of the Coastal groups have mythical traditions containing episodes in which the hero of a story feigns bleeding at the mouth by chewing pieces of red alder bark and letting the saliva ooze from his lips, in order to fool his enemies into believing he was dead.

The Interior peoples commonly used alder bark to treat animal hides. The Lillooet rubbed skins on peeled alder trees to darken their colour from yellowish to reddish-brown. The Okanagan simply rubbed them with the fresh bark. They made a concentrated red paint by boiling the wood in water for a long time, until the liquid had nearly evaporated, then adding a few drops of fish oil, stirring constantly, and finally removing it from the heat and powdering it on a piece of alder bark. This could be used on wood and hides, or as a body paint. The Shuswap and Thompson steeped buckskins overnight in a cooled solution of alder bark, colouring and tanning them at the same time. The Shuswap sometimes mixed the bark with Saskatoon berries to make a dark purple dye for hides. They made a black dye by boiling the bark with roasted iron pyrites. The regular reddish-brown colouring, reportedly the most commonly used pigment of the Shuswap, was employed for dyeing gambling sticks, porcupine quills, hair, feathers, straw, dressed skins, and buckskin clothes. These items were simply soaked in an alder bark solution, taken out and wrung or squeezed dry, then resoaked until the desired shade was obtained. The Flathead of Montana used alder dye to tint moccasins yellow, feathers reddish-brown, and human hair a flaming red.

The importance of alder as a dye is well known, but the utility of the wood is often overlooked. It makes excellent fuel and is considered one of the very best woods for smoking salmon and cooking deer meat because it has a low pitch content and does not impart any unpleasant flavour to the food. The green, fresh wood was not as satisfactory as seasoned or partially rotted wood for this purpose. The Carrier put alder bark chips in with the hot rocks at the bottom of steam-cooking pits; they would burn for many hours with a slow, steady heat. The Okanagan used the burnt ashes of alder and birch to clean their teeth.

The absence of pitchy flavour in the wood and its smooth, even-grained texture made it ideal for carving spoons, and serving platters. Some of the finest examples of Northwest coast bowls and feast dishes are made of red alder. It was also used to carve rattles, masks, head-dresses, arrowpoints, pendants, labrets (ornaments worn on a pierced lower lip), canoe bailers, and paddles. In addition, the Haida carved spoons, small dishes, masks, and rattles from the smaller Sitka alder, and the Kootenay made pipe stems from mountain alder twigs.

The Thompson used the fragrant stems of mountain alder as a scent or perfume. They sometimes used the young twigs for basket imbrication, while the Okanagan made cordage from the bark of young alders and occasionally used the roots as a substitute for red cedar roots in making coiled baskets. They were peeled, split, and soaked in water to make them pliable for weaving. The Carrier wove fishing nets of alder bark, then dyed them black by boiling them in their own juice.

Western White Birch

(Birch Family)

Betula papyrifera Marsh.

(Betulaceae)

OTHER NAMES—Paper birch, western paper birch.

BOTANICAL DESCRIPTION—A small to medium, deciduous tree up to 15–20 m (50–65 ft) high, the young twigs usually hairy and often glandular. The bark when mature is reddish-brown to chalky white, usually peeling readily in horizontal strips and separating into thin layers. The leaf blades, 4–7 cm (1.6–2.8 in.) long, are oval-shaped to nearly round or slightly heart-shaped, sharply pointed, and coarsely or finely toothed. The leaf stalks generally exceed 15 mm (0.6 in.) in length. The flowers are borne in separate male and female catkins, the former long and clustered, the latter shorter and usually single. The catkin scales are shed with the fruits, which are small with lateral wings. A highly variable species, which intergrades freely in southern British Columbia with the closely related water, or black, birch (*B. occidentalis* Hook.). This latter species has less sharply pointed leaves with shorter leaf-stalks and dark, coppery-red to purplish-brown bark which does not separate easily into layers.

HABITAT—Moist, open woods along streams and lake edges from valley bottoms to moderate elevations in the mountains.

DISTRIBUTION IN BRITISH COLUMBIA—Widespread throughout the Interior, and also common in some areas of the Coastal Mainland; rare on Vancouver Island and not found on the Queen Charlotte Islands. At least three varieties are distinguished in the Province.

INDIAN USE—The bark, which can be peeled off the tree in large, flexible, waterproof sheets, was as important to the native peoples of the Interior as the bark of western red cedar was to the Coastal groups. It could be stripped off at any time of the year, but was said to peel most easily in late spring and early summer when the sap was running. Bark with short horizontal lines or lenticels was preferred to that with long lenticels because it would not split and crack when it was being worked on. Only the bark of the western white birch was used; that of the closely related

Western white birch (*Betula papyrifera*).

—Robert D. Turner

196

water birch *(B. occidentalis)*, which is reddish-brown in colour, was not of suitable quality and, being thinner, was more difficult to harvest.

In harvesting the bark, two horizontal cuts were made around the tree, one high and one near the ground, and a single vertical cut was made between them. The sheet was then peeled off by lifting the edges along the cuts and pulling horizontally. When properly done, the harvesting did not kill the tree because only the outer bark was removed, not the innermost layer next to the living cambium tissue. However, often an entire tree would be cut down to collect bark from the upper trunk.

Baskets and canoes were the items most commonly made from birch bark by the Interior peoples. Some of the Coastal groups, including the Upper Stalo and Bella Coola, also made them on occasion, but they learned the craft from their Interior neighbours. Certain Interior groups, such as the Shuswap, were famous for their skill in working with birch bark. Their baskets were widely traded amongst the peoples of the central and southern Interior.

The baskets were constructed by making four diagonal cuts, two from each edge, toward the middle of a rectangular sheet of bark. The sheet was then folded into a box-like shape, with the cuts directed towards the bottom corners and the edges coming together to form side seams. In accordance with the natural tendency of the bark to curl outward when peeled off the tree, the whitish outer surface of the bark formed the inside of the basket and the reddish-brown inner surface formed the basket's exterior. The side seams were sewn, usually with split cedar or spruce root or willow bark, and a circular hoop of the same material or of willow, cedar, red-osier dogwood, or some other flexible wood, was bound or stitched to the top. Finally the seams were caulked with pitch, and designs, some of them very intricate, were etched on the outer surface. Birch-bark containers were made in a variety of sizes and could be used for picking berries, storing food, boiling food by the hot rock method, and even for packing water. In cooking, green sticks of Saskatoon berry or some other shrub were laid in the bottom of the basket to prevent the hot rocks from burning through the birch bark.

Okanagan birch-bark basket sewn with split roots (#II-B-17,
National Museum of Man, Ottawa).

—Dorothy I. D. Kennedy

Canoes were also made from a single piece of bark, folded and sewn onto a frame of willow or cedar withes. The seams and cracks were sealed with pitch. Some of the canoes were 4.5 m (15 ft) or more in length. They were strong yet buoyant and with proper handling were capable of tremendous speeds. Some of the canoes made by Athapaskan groups such as the Carrier were so skilfully constructed that they could be dismantled and folded for portaging.

Birch bark was also used for wrapping foods for storage, lining graves and covering corpses, splinting broken limbs, binding implements, and as roofing for temporary shelters. The Lillooet placed funnel-shaped circles of birch bark around the poles of raised food caches to protect them from climbing rodents. The Tahltan made snow goggles from the bark, the Beaver made moose calls, and the Carrier made toboggans. The Lillooet, Thompson, Shuswap, and other groups made birch-bark infant carriers, cradles, and urine conduits but the watertight qualities of the bark made it hot and uncomfortable for babies in the summer.

Birch wood, of uniform texture, strong, and close-grained, but not durable, was employed in a variety of capacities. The Lillooet carved dishes, cups, spoons, and digging-stick handles from it. The Carrier used it to make mauls, digging sticks, and snowshoe frames, and the Tahltan for snowshoe frames and ground sticks, bows, and gambling sticks. Birch-wood snowshoes were said to be excellent for dry snow but absorbed moisture and became too heavy in wet snow. The Beaver sometimes used birch for arrows. On the Nass River, the Niska made birch-wood spoons and masks and twisted ropes from the roots for lashing fishing weirs. The Haida imported birch wood from the Nass to make seaweed-chopping blocks, used in the traditional preparation of the edible *Porphyra* seaweed. Some Kootenay people have recently used birch wood for smoking bacon. Both western white birch and water birch were used as a general fuel by the Okanagan, Shuswap, and other Interior groups.

The Shuswap steeped birch leaves in water to make a shampoo, and mixed birch leaves, children's urine, and alkali clay from the edges of certain lakes to make soap for washing the skin.

Hazelnut
(Birch Family)

Corylus cornuta Marsh.

(Betulaceae)

OTHER NAMES—Wild filbert, cobnut.

BOTANICAL DESCRIPTION—A bushy shrub, usually 2–5 m (6.5–16.5 ft) tall, spreading and profusely branching. The young twigs are woolly. The leaves are broadly oval-shaped, pointed, and sharply toothed. The male flowers are borne in long, yellowish catkins, ripening in early spring. The nuts are borne singly or in

Hazelnut (*Corylus cornuta*).

—Robert D. Turner

clusters of two or three at the ends of twigs. They are encased in long, tubular husks, light green and covered with stiff, prickly hairs. When ripe, the nuts resemble commercial filberts.

HABITAT—Shaded forests on the Coast to open rocky areas in the Interior.

DISTRIBUTION IN BRITISH COLUMBIA—Widespread throughout the southern part of the Province from Vancouver Island to the Kootenays, extending into the northern Interior.

INDIAN USE—The young, straight sucker shoots were used by the Straits Salish and Lower Lillooet to make arrows. The Upper Stalo of the Fraser Valley, and the Chehalis and Skokomish of Washington, peeled these shoots, twisted them until soft and pliable, and used them singly or as a three-ply rope for tying and lashing. The Shuswap and Gitksan in the Interior used the fresh branches as matting for cleaning salmon on and sitting and sleeping on. The Shuswap used the suckers as edging for birch-bark baskets and cradles and made spoons from the wood because it had no strong flavour. A hazelnut branch with a secondary twig still attached was sometimes used by the Shuswap as a fish-hook. The Gitksan made hockey sticks from bent hazelnut roots. The Okanagan sometimes used hazelnut saplings to make fish traps, tying them together with Indian hemp string. A blue dye, used to colour basket materials, was obtained from the roots by the Thompson, and from the inner bark by the Sanpoil-Nespelem Okanagan of Washington, by steeping these tissues in water.

Stoneseed   *Lithospermum incisum* **Lehm.**
                               and *L. ruderale* Dougl. ex Lehm.

(Borage Family)   **(Boraginaceae)**

OTHER NAMES—Gromwell, puccoon, lemonweed, Indian paint.

BOTANICAL DESCRIPTION—*Lithospermum incisum* is a perennial herb with leafy stems up to 3 dm (12 in.) tall, ascending from a woody taproot. The leaves are linear or lance-shaped, 2–6 cm (0.8–2.4 in.) long, numerous, and crowded along the stems. Both

Stoneseed (*Lithospermum ruderale*).

—Nancy J. Turner

stems and leaves are covered with stiff, sharp hairs. The flowers are bright yellow, tubular, and showy, borne in the axils of the uppermost leaves, or, later in the season, on the lower portion of the stems. The fruits are nutlets which are hard, pitted, pointed, and shiny, resembling white enamelled teeth. *Lithospermum ruderale* is similar, but generally taller and bushier with smaller, light yellow flowers and smooth nutlets. (A common synonym for *L. incisum* is *L. angustifolium* Michx.)

HABITAT—Both species grow on dry, open plains and foothills in rocky or gravelly soil. *Lithospermum ruderale* is also found on upland meadows, such as at Botanie Valley.

DISTRIBUTION IN BRITISH COLUMBIA—Both occur in the dry southern Interior.

INDIAN USE—The roots of *L. incisum,* which are red at the tips, were used by the Thompson, Lillooet, Shuswap, and the Blackfoot of Alberta, to make a red paint for inscribing designs and pictures on dressed skins, gambling sticks, bows, and faces. The roots were dipped in hot grease and used to paint on the colour directly. When first applied the paint is blood red, but it fades with age to a dull purple or violet. The Lillooet and probably other groups fixed the colour by rubbing it with the heated stems of prickly pear cactus. The Thompson name for this plant means "bloody," and one of the common names, puccoon, was derived from an Algon-kian Indian term for plants used for staining and dyeing. The Blackfoot dried the tops and seeds of this plant as an incense.

Lithospermum ruderale roots, and possibly also those of *L. incisum,* were used by the Okanagan as a red dye. The Shuswap used a red fluid from the stems of *L. ruderale* to make a deadly poison for arrow tips, said to kill a person at a touch. This fluid, reportedly very rare and difficult to obtain, was steeped in hot water to produce the poison. Okanagan fishermen drew their lines through a handful of this plant to give them good luck in fishing. It probably had the effect of masking any human odour on the lines. Children used the shiny white nutlets as beads.

Prickly-pear Cactus   ***Opuntia fragilis*** **(Nutt.)**
                                   Haw. and *O. polyacantha* Haw.

(Cactus Family)   **(Cactaceae)**

BOTANICAL DESCRIPTION—Low-growing perennials, often spreading into mats several metres broad. The stems are jointed and succulent, covered with clusters of a few rigid, long spines, up to 5 cm (2 in.) in length, arising from cushions of numerous short bristles. The flowers are 5–7 cm (2–3 in.) long, yellow, sometimes turning pinkish with age, with many petals and stamens, and very showy. The fruits are small, dry, reddish, and spiny. The stem segments of *O. fragilis* are round in cross-section and usually 2–5 cm (0.4–2.0 in.) long, while those of *O. polyacantha* are strongly flattened and mostly 5–15 cm (2–6 in.) long.

HABITAT—Dry hillsides and open plains.

DISTRIBUTION IN BRITISH COLUMBIA—Both species are common in the dry valleys and hillsides of the southern Interior, *O. fragilis* extending north into the Peace River region. Both species also occur on the rocky points of southern Vancouver Island and the Gulf Islands.

INDIAN USE—The Okanagan placed rings of cactus around the supporting poles of raised caches to keep mice and other animals from climbing up. They used the sharp spines to pierce ears and, when bones for fish-hooks were unavailable, they joined two cactus spines together in a V-shape or four together in a "cross" to make a temporary hook. Indian hemp string was used to tie the spines and the joint was sealed with pitch. The Shuswap also made fish hooks in this manner. The mucilaginous juice from the inside of the cactus stems was used by the Lillooet and the Blackfoot of Alberta to fix painted designs on wood and buckskin, and by the Thompson to make face paints stay on longer. The freshly

Prickly-pear cactus (*Opuntia fragilis*).

—Nancy J. Turner

cut stems were heated and rubbed over surfaces painted with vegetable pigments such as stoneseed root or with mineral ochre colours. The Blackfoot also employed the sticky juice to clear muddy water. They placed a cut cactus stem in a container of the water and agitated the mixture, allowing the silt particles to become entrapped in the mucilage of the stem. The flat, disk-shaped seeds were strung and worn as necklaces by Thompson women.

Orange Honeysuckle	*Lonicera ciliosa* (Pursh) DC.
(Honeysuckle Family)	(Caprifoliaceae)

BOTANICAL DESCRIPTION—A shrubby vine, twining on other shrubs and trees, sometimes to a height of 6 m (20 ft) or more. The bark is light greyish-brown and stringy. The leaves, in opposite pairs, are ellipse-shaped, pointed or rounded, and smooth-edged, the terminal pair fused into a single concave disk or cup, subtending the flower cluster. The undersides of the leaves and young stems are covered with a whitish waxy coating, giving them a light blue-green colour. The tubular flowers, in tight clusters, are bright orange and showy. The fruits are soft, fleshy, orange- or coral-red berries. Flowering time is in the summer; the fruits ripen in August and September.

HABITAT—Roadside thickets and open woods from sea level to moderate elevations in the mountains.

DISTRIBUTION IN BRITISH COLUMBIA—Common in the southern parts of the Province, especially west of the Cascade Mountains.

INDIAN USE—The Thompson, and possibly other Interior Salish groups, used the stem fibre, usually mixed with some other type of fibre, for weaving mats, bags, capes, aprons, and blankets. They employed the woody vines for reinforcing suspension bridges over the Fraser, Thompson, and other rivers. The Flathead of Montana boiled the stems to make a shampoo, said to make the hair grow longer.

Orange honeysuckle (*Lonicera ciliosa*).

—Harold Hosford

Black Twinberry

Lonicera involucrata
(Rich.) Banks.

(Honeysuckle Family)

(Caprifoliaceae)

OTHER NAMES—Twin-flower honeysuckle, fly honeysuckle, "bearberry," bearberry honeysuckle.

BOTANICAL DESCRIPTION—A bushy shrub up to 3 m (10 ft) or more high, with light brown, shredding bark, and paired, pointed, ellipse-shaped leaves. The flowers are yellow, tubular and paired. Each pair is closely subtended by two pairs of thin,

Black twinberry (*Lonicera involucrata*).

—Robert D. Turner

leafy bracts which turn bright red or purplish as the fruits mature. The fleshy twin-berries are black, shiny, and bead-like. Flowers may be found on the bushes from April through August, with berries ripening from July to September.

HABITAT—Moist thickets and open, swampy areas from sea level to subalpine elevations.

DISTRIBUTION IN BRITISH COLUMBIA—Widespread throughout the Province, especially on the Coast and in the Interior wet belt; sporadic but locally abundant.

INDIAN USE—The purple juice from the berries was used by various groups as a pigment. The Shuswap used it to dye roots for basketry, and the Quileute of Washington used it to paint dolls' faces. The Kwakiutl mashed the berries with salal berries to intensify the colour. The Haida rubbed the berries into the scalp as a tonic to prevent the hair from turning grey. They sometimes made gambling sticks from the wood.

Red Elderberry and	***Sambucus racemosa* L.**
Blue Elderberry	**and *S. cerulea* Raf.**
(Honeysuckle Family)	**(Caprifoliaceae)**

BOTANICAL DESCRIPTION—These are tall, bushy shrubs with greyish-brown bark and brittle, pithy twigs. The leaves are compound, with 5–9 pointed, toothed, lance- to oval-shaped leaflets. The flowers are small and creamy-white, in large clusters, which are pyramidal in *S. racemosa* and flat-topped in *S. cerulea*. The berries of *S. racemosa* are bright red; those of *S. cerulea* are deep blue with a waxy whitish bloom. (*Sambucus racemosa* is also known as *S. pubens* Michx.; *S. cerulea* is also called *S. glauca* Nutt. ex T. & G.)

HABITAT—*S. racemosa* occurs in open, swampy areas, moist clearings and shaded woods, while *S. cerulea* is found on valley bottoms and open slopes. Both grow from sea level to moderate elevations in the mountains.

DISTRIBUTION IN BRITISH COLUMBIA—*S. racemosa* is widespread along the Coast, extending into the Interior along some of

Red elderberry (*Sambucus racemosa*).

—Robert D. Turner

the major river valleys and recurring in the Interior wet belt; *S. cerulea* occurs on southeastern Vancouver Island and in the Fraser Valley, and is abundant in the southern Interior.

INDIAN USE—While they are easily hollowed-out, and were widely used by the Indian peoples as whistles, drinking straws, blowguns, and pipestems, the stems, roots, and foliage of the elderberries are poisonous, therefore their use for such items is not recommended. The Straits Salish made pipe stems and the Bella Coola pipe bowls from red elderberry, and the children of these and other groups, such as the Kwakiutl, made blowguns, equivalent to the modern "pea shooter." They employed small pieces of kelp or other vegetation as ammunition. The Lillooet used both red and blue elderberry for making blowguns, and the Okanagan used blue elderberry for blowguns, and for the drinking straws used by girls at puberty. The Sanpoil-Nespelem Okanagan of Washington and the Flathead of Montana made small flutes or "flageolets," the former group from blue elderberry, the latter from both blue and red elderberry. The Quinault of Washington made elk whistles from blue elderberry stems and the Lillooet sometimes made urine conduits for baby carriers from red elderberry, and probably from blue elderberry as well, when birch bark was not available.

The Haida used red elderberry pith to fasten flint tips onto arrow shafts, while the Kwakiutl fixed segments of the stem onto arrows used to stun birds. They also used pieces of the stem as bases for feather shuttlecocks, employed in a certain game. The Mainland Comox made 6-inch long ling cod lures from pieces of red elderberry stem hollowed out, with several seagull feathers inserted at one end. The Sanpoil-Nespelem Okanagan sometimes used the straighter branches of the blue elderberry to make temporary arrows for small game.

| **Waxberry** | ***Symphoricarpos albus* (L.) Blake** |
| **(Honeysuckle Family)** | **(Caprifoliaceae)** |

OTHER NAME—Snowberry.

BOTANICAL DESCRIPTION—An erect, branching shrub, 1–2 m (3–6 ft) tall, with greyish bark. The leaves are opposite, elliptic or oval-shaped, mostly 1.5–5 cm (0.6–2.0 in.) long, often irregularly lobed, especially those on new twigs and suckers. The flowers are small, urn-shaped, whitish or pink, in dense, few-flowered clusters. The fruits are berrylike, white, globular, and fleshy, often remaining on the bushes over the winter.

HABITAT—Thickets, woods, and open areas from sea level to moderate elevations in the mountains.

DISTRIBUTION IN BRITISH COLUMBIA—Widespread throughout the Province.

INDIAN USE—The Okanagan, Shuswap, the Blackfoot of Alberta, and probably other groups as well, used the branches to make brooms. The bushy twigs were bound together in a tight bundle, and were sometimes tied onto a long stick for a handle. The Shuswap and Gitksan hollowed out the twigs and used them as pipe stems, the pipe bowls were made of flint or soapstone. The Haida used the sticks, peeled, trimmed and sharpened, to string clams, cockles, and mussels on for drying. The Blackfoot of Alberta used the slender branches to make arrow shafts, but the Kootenay considered them a bad material for arrows, as evidenced by an episode in one of their traditional myths in which Coyote showed his ignorance by using waxberry wood to make an arrow. The Blackfoot made a fire from green waxberry twigs and used the smoke to blacken the surface of newly made pipes before they were greased and polished.

Flowering Dogwood	***Cornus nuttallii***
	Aud. ex T. & G.
(Dogwood Family)	**(Cornaceae)**

OTHER NAMES—Pacific, mountain, or western flowering dogwood, Pacific dogwood.

BOTANICAL DESCRIPTION—A handsome, small to moderate sized tree up to 20 m (65 ft) high, or sometimes shrublike. The bark is smooth and greyish, and the branches are whorled. The leaf blades are oval to elliptic, pointed, and smooth-edged, with prominent veins. The leaves turn a bright peach colour in the fall. The flowers are numerous, small, and greenish, in compact, button-like heads, which are subtended by 4–6 large, showy, white bracts. The flower heads begin to form in the fall, maturing in the spring as the leaves expand. Some trees produce a second crop of flowers in the fall. The fruits are bright red-orange, elongated, and berrylike, in compact clusters. This is the Provincial flower of British Columbia.

Flowering dogwood (*Cornus nuttallii*).

HABITAT—Moist, open to shaded woods and slopes, at low elevations.

DISTRIBUTION IN BRITISH COLUMBIA—Common on southern Vancouver Island and the adjacent Mainland, eastward in the Fraser Canyon toward Lytton.

INDIAN USE—The wood is hard and tough but not very durable. It was the main bow-making material of the Lower Lillooet in the Pemberton Valley, far more important in that area than western yew, according to modern informants. It was also used by the Lower Lillooet for making arrows and combs. The Thompson made bows and implement handles from it, and the Cowichan on Vancouver Island used it for making bows, arrows, and, recently, knitting needles. In Washington, the Skagit, Klallam, and Green River groups used it to make gambling disks, the Skagit to make harpoon shafts, and the Snohomish to make bracken rhizome beating sticks. The Straits Salish used the bark as a tanning agent and the Thompson used it to make a deep brown dye. They also mixed it with grand fir bark to make a black dye for colouring bitter cherry bark, which was used in basket imbrication.

Red-osier Dogwood	*Cornus stolonifera* **Michx.**
	var. *occidentalis* **(T. & G.)**
	C. L. Hitchc.
(Dogwood Family)	**(Cornaceae)**

OTHER NAMES—Western dogwood, "red willow," creek dogwood.

BOTANICAL DESCRIPTION—This is a many-stemmed shrub 2–6 m (6.5–20 ft) tall, with smooth, greenish to bright red or reddish-purple bark. The leaf blades are smooth-edged, pointed, oval to elliptic, with prominent, evenly spaced lateral veins. The leaves turn bright red in the fall. The flowers are small and white, in dense, flat-topped clusters. The fruits are round and white to light blue with a fleshy exterior and a hard central stone.

HABITAT—Moist soil, in marshes and swamps, and along streams and lake edges from sea level to near timberline.

DISTRIBUTION IN BRITISH COLUMBIA—Widespread throughout the Province in appropriate habitats.

INDIAN USE—The thin, flexible branches were employed in a variety of capacities by British Columbia Indians. The Shuswap used them as salmon-stretchers and skewers for barbecuing salmon. They were said to impart a salty flavour to the flesh. They were also used by the Shuswap to make the rims of birch-bark and cedar-root baskets, to make a grid to hold the food being cooked in a steaming basket, to secure the frames of sweathouses, and to make fish traps and weirs. The wood was considered a good fuel for smoking and drying meat and fish because it doesn't blacken the meat; it was also used along with Saskatoon wood as a fuel for drying huckleberries. The Okanagan used the branches to construct fish traps and weirs and made spatulas, cooking grids, and skewers from them as well. The Kootenay used them for pelt

Red-osier dogwood (*Cornus stolonifera*).

—Nancy J. Turner

stretchers, and the Flathead of Montana to construct sweathouses. The Bella Coola made barbecue racks from them and the Haida used them to make drying racks and other types of frames. The Blackfoot of Alberta made pipe stems and tamps from the sticks.

The bark fibre was used as cordage for tying and lashing by both the Okanagan and the Shuswap. The bark was stripped off and the pieces twisted and spliced together, or sometimes the entire branch was twisted, the wood adding strength to the rope. It was used to bind underwater implements, to tie fish traps, barbecue sticks and smokehouse frame poles, and as latticework for fish weirs. The Okanagan mixed the powdered bark with the resin of cottonwood buds to make a red paint.

Silverberry   *Elaeagnus commutata* Bernh.
(Oleaster Family)   (Elaeagnaceae)

OTHER NAMES—Silver buffalo berry, sometimes called "silver willow," or "pink-barked willow."

BOTANICAL DESCRIPTION—An erect, bushy shrub 1–4 m (3–13 ft) high with smooth, greyish-brown to pinkish bark and silvery-scurfy leaves 2–7 cm (0.8–2.8 in.) long, which are lance-shaped to elliptic, pointed, and smooth-edged. The flowers, which bloom in early summer, are small, yellow, and tubular, with a distinctive, almost overpowering odour, enjoyed by some and considered disagreeable by others. They are borne in small clusters in the leaf axils. The fruits are spherical, silvery, and pithy with a hard central stone.

HABITAT—Open, gravelly slopes and benchlands, and along gulleys and watercourses.

DISTRIBUTION IN BRITISH COLUMBIA—Most abundant along watercourses in the dry southern Interior, but extends northward to Alaska and the Yukon.

INDIAN USE—The bark is tough and fibrous and was, for the Interior Salish people and the Kootenay, an important weaving and rope-making material. It was stripped off with a knife, usually

Silverberry (*Elaeagnus commutata*).

—Robert D. Turner

Silverberry bark and berries.

—Robert D. Turner

A Thompson bag of braided strands of silverberry bark, twined with Indian hemp. The dark strands are dyed with the juice of Saskatoon berries (#II-C-618, National Museum of Man, Ottawa).

—Dorothy I. D. Kennedy

in spring. The outer part was discarded and the stringy inner layers were soaked in water and spun on the bare thigh into twine. This was woven into bags, baskets, nets, mats, blankets, and clothing, or plaited into rope for binding and tying and for use as fishing line. The Thompson and Okanagan were especially proficient in the preparation and utilization of this fibre. They braided strands of it and intertwined it with other fibres such as big sagebrush bark, Indian hemp, and white clematis bark. It was often dyed with Oregon grape bark, Saskatoon berries, and other pigments. The Okanagan and Shuswap sometimes made soapberry beaters from it by tying a bunch of it onto a short handle. It was said that in the old trading days in Okanagan country, three five-inch thick bundles of prepared silverberry bark were worth a blanket. The large, silvery fruits were strung and used as beads for necklaces and for decorating clothing by the Thompson, Okanagan, Kootenay, and the Blackfoot of Alberta. The Blackfoot rubbed them with grease and often interspersed them with juniper berries.

Pacific Madrone	***Arbutus menziesii* Pursh**
(Heather Family)	**(Ericaceae)**

OTHER NAMES—Arbutus, madrona.

BOTANICAL DESCRIPTION—A branching, often twisted and knarled, broad-leafed evergreen tree, 6–30 m (20–100 ft) high. The bark is smooth and satiny, bright green when young, and maturing to a deep brownish-red. It is shed annually from the upper trunk and branches in large, paperlike sheets. The glossy, deep green leaves are leathery, oval to elliptic, 7–15 cm (2.8–6.0 in.) long, and smooth-edged or finely toothed. They remain on the trees throughout the winter, turning yellow and dropping the following summer after the next season's leaves are completely developed. The flowers, which mature in spring, are white and urn-shaped, in dense sprays. The berries, about 1 cm (0.4 in.) across, are bright red-orange, with a textured surface. They often remain on the trees well into winter.

Pacific Madrone (*Arbutus menziesii*).

—Robert D. Turner

HABITAT—Open, moderately dry, woods and rocky bluffs, at lower elevations.

DISTRIBUTION IN BRITISH COLUMBIA—On southeastern Vancouver Island and the Gulf Islands, and the adjacent Mainland west of the Coast and Cascade Mountains, from Bute Inlet southward.

INDIAN USE—The wood is too hard and brittle and checks too easily to be of much value for carving. However, the Straits Salish, specifically the Saanich, formerly used the young branches to make spoons and gambling sticks. Recently the Sechelt used the wood to construct the sterns and keels of small boats because it is durable under water. The Saanich placed the bark in steaming pits with camas bulbs to colour them pink. The Saanich and Cowichan boiled the bark as a tanning agent for paddles and fish hooks. In the early days the Saanich strung the berries for necklaces.

Wild Gooseberries	*Ribes divaricatum* **Dougl.** and other *Ribes* **species**
(Gooseberry Family)	**(Grossulariaceae)**

OTHER NAME—*Ribes divaricatum* is known as common wild gooseberry.

BOTANICAL DESCRIPTION—*Ribes divaricatum* is a stout, branching, deciduous shrub usually under 2 m (6.5 ft) high, with smooth, greyish bark and 1–3 sharp spines at each stem node. The leaves are small and maple-leaf shaped, with 3–5 main lobes. The flowers are drooping, with deep-red sepals, white petals, and protruding stamens. The fruits are smooth and purplish-black when ripe. There are several other wild gooseberry species in the Province, all with the same general characteristics: short, bushy shrubs with spiny branches, palmately lobed leaves, and dark, drooping berries. One species, *R. inerme,* is very similar, differing only in a few minor features, such as the length and colour of the calyx lobes, which are slightly shorter and paler.

Wild gooseberry (*Ribes inerme*).

—Robert D. Turner

HABITAT—Gooseberries grow in a variety of habitats. *Ribes divaricatum* is found in moist sites, in woods and clearings.

DISTRIBUTION IN BRITISH COLUMBIA—*Ribes divaricatum* is common on southeastern Vancouver Island, the Gulf Islands, and the Lower Mainland west of the Cascade Mountains, extending northward up the Coast and eastward up some of the major river valleys. *R. inerme* occurs on the east slopes of the Cascades. Various gooseberry species are found throughout the Province.

INDIAN USE—Most Indian people do not distinguish among the different species of gooseberries, especially those with similar spine characteristics. The Straits Salish (Saanich) and the Halkomelem (Cowichan) of Vancouver Island used gooseberry thorns as probes for opening boils, for removing slivers, and for tattooing. The Cowichan boiled the roots with red cedar roots and wild rose roots and wove them together into rope, used for making reefnets.

The Bella Coola hollowed out the stems of *R. divaricatum* to make pipe stems, with or without a bowl of elderberry wood. In the Interior, the Shuswap carved combs from the wood of one species of gooseberry and the Kootenay made fish hooks from gooseberry thorns, probably those of *R. irriguum* Dougl.

Mock-orange	*Philadelphus lewisii* Pursh
(Hydrangea Family)	(Hydrangeaceae)

OTHER NAMES — Syringa, wild orange, soap plant, "white maple."

BOTANICAL DESCRIPTION—A handsome deciduous shrub up to 3 m (10 ft) tall, with light brown, shredding bark and pale green, lance-shaped to elliptic, pointed, coarsely toothed leaves usually 2.5–7.0 cm (1.0–2.8 in.) long. The flowers are white with yellow centres, 4-petalled, and showy, in dense terminal clusters. In fragrance and appearance they resemble orange blossoms, hence the popular name. The fruits are oval, pointed capsules, dark brown and hard when mature.

HABITAT—Shaded to open woods, gullies, talus slopes, and rocky hillsides from sea level to subalpine elevations.

DISTRIBUTION IN BRITISH COLUMBIA—In the southern part of the Province, both on the Coast and in the Interior. The Interior form is generally shorter and bushier, with less fragrant flowers than the Coastal form.

INDIAN USE—The wood is strong and "hard as a bone," never cracking or warping when properly prepared. It was widely used for making implements, especially among the Interior Salish. The Okanagan used it for spear shafts, bows and arrows, digging sticks, "sliding" snowshoes, and clubs, as well as for pipe stems and cradle hoops. The Shuswap made digging sticks, combs, imitation breast-bone decorations, fish spears and bearpaw-type snowshoes from it. They sometimes obtained the wood from neighbouring Lillooet groups. The Lillooet used it mainly to make digging sticks but Sam Mitchell of the Fountain Reserve described how he made long knitting needles for his wife from a one-inch thick stem. He split

Mock-orange (*Philadelphus lewisii*).

—Tom Sowerby

it in quarters, carved and sanded the pieces, fire-hardened the points, then polished them. Children of the Lower Lillooet made blowguns from the larger stems by hollowing out the pithy inner core. The Thompson used the wood for making combs and as edging for birch-bark baskets and cradle hoods. The Kootenay made huckleberry-picking combs from it, and the Flathead of Montana made combs, pipe stems, bows, and arrow shafts. On the Coast, the Saanich sometimes used the wood for bows and arrows, and the Lummi of Washington, also a Straits Salish group, made combs, netting shuttles, and knitting needles from it. The Cowlitz of Washington made combs from it and the Skagit, arrow shafts.

The leaves foam into a lather when bruised and rubbed with the hands. This was used as a soap for cleansing the skin by the

Okanagan, Shuswap, and Lillooet, and by the Cowlitz and Sno-homish of Washington, who also used the crushed flowers. The Shuswap obtained a lather from the bark as well by soaking it in warm water. They used the leaves for washing clothing.

The blooming of this bush was a traditional indicator to the Okanagan that the "groundhogs" (yellow-bellied marmots) were fat and ready to be hunted.

Fireweed	*Epilobium angustifolium* **L.**
(Evening Primrose Family)	**(Onagraceae)**

OTHER NAMES—Willow herb, blooming Sally.

BOTANICAL DESCRIPTION—A tall, smooth-stemmed, herbaceous perennial, with spreading roots and alternate, smooth-edged, lance-shaped leaves resembling those of narrow-leaved willows. The flowers are 4-petalled, red-purple, and very showy, growing in long, terminal clusters. They bloom throughout the summer, in sequence from bottom to top. The seed capsules are long and narrow, splitting longitudinally on all four sides to reveal rows of small, parachuted seeds. These travel on the wind for long distances.

HABITAT—Growing in extensive patches in open clearings, logged-off areas, burns, and along roadsides. In summer the flowers often colour entire hillsides pink.

DISTRIBUTION IN BRITISH COLUMBIA—Widespread throughout the Province.

INDIAN USE—The Haida used the outer stem-fibres, discarded when the inner tissue was eaten, to make cordage. The "skin" of the stem was peeled off, dried, and later soaked in water and twisted or spun into twine, used especially for making fishing nets. Several Coast Salish groups used the seed fluff or "cotton" mixed with other materials for weaving and padding. The Saanich and other Vancouver Island groups and the Squamish of the Main-land added it to the wool of small domesticated dogs and wove the mixture into blankets and clothing. According to one source, only higher class women of the Saanich group made clothing with dog's

Fireweed (*Epilobium angustifolium*).

—Nancy J. Turner

wool and fireweed cotton. They first beat the dog's wool with diatomaceous earth, presumably to clean it. The Squamish also wove the cotton with mountain goat wool. The Saanich stuffed mattresses with a mixture of fireweed fluff and duck feathers. In Washington, most Puget Sound groups also used fireweed 'cotton' for weaving, mixing it with mountain goat wool. The Quinault and Skokomish used it mixed with duck feathers to make blankets.

Fireweed leaves were sometimes used by the Carrier to cover baskets full of berries. The Blackfoot of Alberta rubbed the flowers on rawhide thongs and mittens to waterproof them. They applied the powdered inner cortex to the hands and face in the winter to protect them from the cold.

White Clematis	*Clematis ligusticifolia* **Nutt.**
(Buttercup Family)	**(Ranunculaceae)**

OTHER NAMES—White virgin's bower, pipestems, traveler's joy.

BOTANICAL DESCRIPTION—A woody, climbing vine with stems up to 20 m (65 ft) long, often forming dense clumps along fences and thickets. The bark is greyish-brown and stringy. The leaves are pinnately compound, with 5–7 oval, pointed, coarsely toothed leaflets. The plants are "dioecious"—male and female flowers are borne on separate vines. Both types of flowers are creamy-white, in few- to many-flowered clusters, usually very showy. The blooming period extends from May through August; often flowers and fruits are seen simultaneously on the same plant. Each fruit—and there are several per flower—bears a long, white plume, which aids in dispersal. In combination, these form large clouds of soft, silvery fluff, even more conspicuous than the flower clusters. They remain on the vines late into the fall.

HABITAT—Roadsides and creekbottoms, climbing on fences, shrubs, and trees, or trailing over the ground, often forming dense thickets.

DISTRIBUTION IN BRITISH COLUMBIA—Common throughout the dry southern Interior and also found on southern Vancouver Island and the Gulf Islands.

White clematis (*Clematis ligusticifolia*).

—Robert D. Turner

INDIAN USE—The Okanagan and Thompson stripped off the stringy bark fibre and used it for weaving bags, mats, capes, and other garments. It was often interwoven or twined with other plant materials, such as Indian hemp or silverberry bark. It was said that a good clematis bag could withstand weights of 75 to 100 pounds. In the old days the Shuswap used the vines, still growing, to straighten and strengthen implement handles. They would locate a clematis plant and place the handle into the centre, twining the stems around it. It was left for up to two years, allowing the clematis to entwine it completely. At the end of this time it was disentangled and used as the handle of a "tomahawk" or some other implement. This treatment was said to keep the handle from warping and make it very strong.

The Okanagan and the Flathead of Montana rubbed the leaves together to form a lather, used as a general soap and as a hair shampoo. The Flathead used the leaves of the blue clematis

A Thompson cape of white clematis bark, twined with Indian hemp (#85700, Field Museum of Natural History, Chicago).

—Dorothy I. D. Kennedy

[*C. columbiana* (Nutt.) T. & G.] for the same purpose. A Kootenay informant noted that the fluffy seedheads were used as nesting material by birds and pikas or "rock rabbits."

Larkspur	*Delphinium bicolor* Nutt. and other *Delphinium* species
(Buttercup Family)	(Ranunculaceae)

BOTANICAL DESCRIPTION—*D. bicolor* is a perennial herb from a cluster of thickened roots. The stems are usually single, 1.5–4 dm (6–16 in.) tall, and the leaves, few in number and mostly basal, are long-stemmed and deeply segmented into wedge-shaped lobed segments. The upper leaves are smaller, with fewer segments. The sepals are deep blue and widely flared, the uppermost being modified into a distinctive hollow "spur," characteristic of the genus. The petals are shorter than the sepals; the upper two are pale blue, the others darker. The fruits are long, pointed follicles, 3 per flower, each splitting along one side and containing numerous flattened, dark-coloured seeds. Several other species of *Delphinium* closely resemble this one in form and colour.

HABITAT—Gravelly, well-drained soil from grasslands and ponderosa pine woods to subalpine slopes.

DISTRIBUTION IN BRITISH COLUMBIA—In the extreme southern Interior from the lower Okanagan Valley to the Rocky Mountains. Other species of *Delphinium* are distributed throughout the Province.

INDIAN USE—The Okanagan used the bright blue flowers of this and other species of larkspur as a blue dye for colouring arrows and other items. The Thompson also used the flowers of a species of larkspur as a blue colouring, even for dyeing clothing, but they were reported by some to be of little value. The Blackfoot of Alberta mixed the flowers with water and used the solution to dye porcupine quills. Recently the Shuswap used larkspur flowers mixed with roses for the Corpus Christi procession in the church. They were scattered by small girls.

Saskatoon Berry

(Rose Family)

Amelanchier alnifolia **Nutt.**

(Rosaceae)

OTHER NAMES—Serviceberry, June berry, shad-bush.

BOTANICAL DESCRIPTION—A highly variable, deciduous shrub, 1–7 m (3–23 ft) high, with smooth, reddish to grey bark and numerous round to oval-shaped leaves. These are bluish-green and usually sharply toothed around the top half. The flowers, which bloom in April and May, are white and showy, with five elongated petals and crowded in drooping to erect clusters. Especially in the Interior, the flowers often cover the bushes, creating a spectacular sight in areas where the plants are numerous. The berries, when ripe, are reddish-purple to dark blue, and often seedy. The size, texture and taste vary considerably from plant to plant. Botanists distinguish three varieties within the Province —var. *alnifolia,* var. *semiintegrifolia* (Hook.) C. L. Hitchc., and var. *cusickii* (Fern.) C. L. Hitchc., while Indian peoples delineate up to eight different types. Further taxonomic research on this highly complex species may reveal the native peoples to be more accurate in their designation than botanists have been.

HABITAT—Dry woods and open hillsides, in well-drained soil.

DISTRIBUTION IN BRITISH COLUMBIA—Common and widespread throughout the Province, but most prolific in the dry woods and open slopes of the southern Interior.

INDIAN USE—The wood is hard, straight-grained, and tough. It can be rendered even harder by heating it over a fire and is easily moulded while still hot. Its most important use was for making arrows. All of the Interior Salish groups—the Okanagan, Thompson, Shuswap, and Lillooet—as well as the Kootenay, Carrier, Gitksan, Straits Salish, Upper Stalo, and the Flathead of Montana, used it for this purpose. In most of these areas it was the major arrow-making material. A thin, straight branch was chosen and stripped of any leaves or twigs. At least in the Lillooet area it was thoroughly chewed to loosen the bark and break the grain of the wood to prevent it from curling or warping later. The bark was

Saskatoon berry (*Amelanchier alnifolia*).

—Robert D. Turner

231

then removed and the wood was fire-hardened. One end was feathered and the other tipped with a bone, stone, or metal point, or simply sharpened. The surface was polished with horsetail stems, and often designs were painted along the shaft.

Saskatoon wood was also extensively used for making digging sticks, spear and harpoon shafts, and implement handles. The Okanagan also made barbecue sticks and seed beaters from it, and the Shuswap made barbecue sticks, basket frames, and cross-pieces for canoes. Both the Shuswap and the Lillooet placed a grid of green Saskatoon sticks at the bottom of birch-bark cooking baskets to prevent them from being burned through by red-hot rocks. They also used Saskatoon twigs for lining steaming pits and as salmon spreaders for drying and cooking salmon. (The wood is said not to give a bitter flavour to the fish.) The Lillooet commonly constructed shelters from the branches for drying salmon and berries. The Carrier made slat armour and shields from the wood, covering them with animal hide, and wove mats from the branches on which to dry berries. On the Coast, the Saanich used Saskatoon to make herring rakes, and the Stalo, along the Fraser River, to make eulachon rakes. The ends of these rakes were studded with rows of spikes, to impale the fish as the implement was swept through the water.

The berries were mashed and used by the Thompson and other Interior Salish peoples to stain such materials as silverberry bark, used in making bags.

Red Hawthorn and	*Crataegus columbiana* **Howell**
Black Hawthorn	**and *C. douglasii* Lindl.**
(Rose Family)	**(Rosaceae)**

OTHER NAMES—Red and black thornberry, red and black haw.

BOTANICAL DESCRIPTION—These are bushy, deciduous shrubs or small trees. *C. columbiana* seldom exceeds 3 m (10 ft) in height, while *C. douglasii* may be a metre or more taller. Both shrubs are armed with sharp thorns, those of *C. columbiana* being slender and 4–7 cm (1.6–2.8 in.) long, and those of *C. douglasii*

Red hawthorn (*Crataegus columbiana*).

—Robert D. Turner

being stouter and 1–2 cm (0.4–0.8 in.) long. The leaves are thick, dark green and shiny, being roughly oval-shaped and coarsely toothed. *C. columbiana* leaves are pointed, while those of *C. douglasii* are usually blunter, though sharply toothed across the top. The flowers are white and showy, in flattened clusters, blooming in April and May. The berries of *C. columbiana* are bright red; those of *C. douglasii* are shiny black-purple. They grow in hanging clusters. Fruits of both species have a pleasant, though sometimes astringent flavour. In texture they are mealy and both have large seeds.

HABITAT—Both are species of meadows and stream courses to dry hillsides and gullies.

DISTRIBUTION IN BRITISH COLUMBIA—*C. columbiana* is found in the southern Interior, from Prince George southward through the Okanagan and Kootenay valleys, and also occurs in the Peace River District; *C. douglasii* is common throughout the Province south of latitude 55°N.

INDIAN USE—The spines of both species were used by the Thompson and Okanagan as needles for probing boils and skin ulcers, and for piercing ears. Red hawthorn spines were used as pins in an Okanagan "ball and pin" game (the ball was made of tule stem). The Thompson made fish hooks from them, while the Lillooet and Gitksan made fish hooks from black hawthorn spines. The wood of the red hawthorn was little used, but that of black hawthorn, which is tough and hard, was used by the Okanagan, Lillooet and Shuswap, and by the Blackfoot of Alberta, to make digging sticks, by the Okanagan and Lillooet for clubs, by the Shuswap for axe handles, dipnet handles, and double-trees for horse-drawn wagons and by the Carrier and Gitksan for adze handles. The Cowichan of Vancouver Island burned the leaves, inner bark, and new shoots of the black hawthorn, mixed the ash with grease or ochre and used it as a black face paint for winter dances.

Oceanspray	*Holodiscus discolor* (**Pursh**) **Maxim.**
(**Rose Family**)	(**Rosaceae**)

OTHER NAMES—Arrow-wood, "ironwood," rock spiraea.

BOTANICAL DESCRIPTION—An erect, deciduous shrub, 1–3 m (about 3–10 ft) tall, with straight, slender branches, the young ones ribbed or angled. The bark is reddish-brown when young, grey on mature stems. The leaves are usually 4–10 cm (1.6–4.0 in.) long, bright green on the upper surface, paler beneath, more or less oval-shaped. The leaf bases are rounded to wedge-shaped, and the margins are shallowly to deeply lobed with 15–25 toothed segments which decrease in size toward the tip. The flowers are small and cream-coloured, in large, pyramidal clusters. These are borne at the ends of the twigs and make a conspicuous

Oceanspray (*Holodiscus discolor*).

—Nancy J. Turner

235

showing during the blooming season, in mid-summer. The fruiting clusters are greyish-brown and wispy, remaining on the bushes over the winter.

HABITAT—Dry, rocky slopes and open woods from sea level to moderate elevations in the mountains.

DISTRIBUTION IN BRITISH COLUMBIA—In the southern part of the Province, both on the Coast and in the Interior, especially common on the rocky bluffs of southeastern Vancouver Island and the Gulf Islands.

INDIAN USE—Most native people call this shrub "ironwood," a name which reflects its hardness and strength. Like Saskatoon wood, it could be made even harder by heating it over a fire. It was used by virtually all of the southern groups—the Straits Salish, Halkomelem or Stalo, Squamish, Sechelt, Kwakiutl, Lillooet, Thompson, Okanagan, and Kootenay—for making digging sticks, and by most of these groups for making spear and harpoon shafts, bows, and arrows. Some groups, such as the Okanagan, bound their bows at the haft with deer sinew for added strength. The wood was usually polished with horsetail stems. Additionally, the Okanagan used it to make teepee pins, gambling sticks, leister prongs, fish clubs, drum hoops, and hoops for baby cradles, the Thompson to make armour, and the Lower Lillooet to make hoops for attaching sinker stones to nets, cross-pieces for Douglas-fir dipnet hoops, and the upper sections on harpoon shafts and gaff-hook handles. The Saanich and Cowichan made salmon barbe-cuing sticks, cambium scrapers, halibut hooks, cat-tail mat needles and, recently, knitting needles, from it, the Squamish made spear prongs, fish hooks, gaff-hook sockets, harpoon foreshafts, clam-drying sticks, stiffeners for cedar-bark canoe bailers, and mat needles, and the Sechelt made fire pokers, drum frames, and clam-drying sticks. In western Washington, ironwood was widely used to make roasting tongs, digging sticks, and spear shafts. The Squaxin even made canoe paddles from it. According to modern informants, neither the Bella Coola nor the Shuswap used the wood, although the bush does occur within their territories.

Bitter Cherry　　　　　　　　　　*Prunus emarginata* (Dougl.)
　　　　　　　　　　　　　　　　　　　　　　Walpers

(Rose Family)　　　　　　　　　　　　　　(Rosaceae)

OTHER NAME—Wild cherry.

BOTANICAL DESCRIPTION—A shrub or erect tree up to 10 m
(33 ft) or more high, deciduous, with smooth, grey to shiny, reddish-
purple bark which peels off the tree in horizontal strips. The leaves
are short-stemmed, 3–8 cm (about 1–3 in.) long, elliptic to oval,
round-tipped or pointed, and often finely toothed. The flowers are
white and relatively small, in few-flowered clusters. The cherries
are small, bright red to almost black, and exceedingly bitter.

HABITAT — Moist woods and clearings, often along watercourses, from sea level to medium elevations in the mountains.

DISTRIBUTION IN BRITISH COLUMBIA—Abundant in the southern part of the Province, especially on the Coast and in the Interior
wet belt.

Bitter cherry (*Prunus emarginata*) with peeled bark.
—Robert D. Turner

A Thompson berry basket of split cedar root imbricated with black-dyed, and natural red, bitter cherry bark, and white grass stems (#85554, Field Museum of Natural History, Chicago).

—Dorothy I. D. Kennedy

INDIAN USE—The tough, shiny bark was widely used by British Columbia Indians to imbricate baskets and to wrap implements for protection and decoration. Among the groups who utilized it were all the Coast and Interior Salish peoples, the Carrier, the Nootka, and the Kwakiutl. It was pulled off the tree in thin, horizontal sheets, or, for wrapping implements, was cut in a continuous spiral. It was usually retained in its natural red colour or was dyed black. The most common method of dyeing was to soak it for several months in rich organic soil, such as in a swamp, or in manure, but it could also be coloured with vegetable dyes, such as flowering dogwood and grand fir bark, used by the Thompson.

The Thompson pounded the bark before it was used to make it soft. Like other Salishan groups, they used strips of dyed and natural bark, along with white and coloured grasses, to create intricate patterns superimposed over the weave of their coiled split-root baskets. They also used cherry bark to imbricate mats and bags, to wrap splints for broken limbs and to reinforce old-time suspension bridges. They also twisted it into twine. The Okanagan, Shuswap, and Lillooet used spirally cut strips of the bark to wrap around the hafts of bows, providing a handgrip and at the same time adding strength. The Okanagan glued the bark in place with fish slime mixed with ochre paint, and sealed the outside with grand fir pitch. They also used strips of the bark to decorate bows, "tomahawk" handles, and pipe stems.

The Lower Lillooet and the Bella Coola, Squamish, Sechelt, Vancouver Island Salish, Nootka, and Kwakiutl used the bark especially for covering the joints of underwater implements such as harpoons, dipnets, gaffhooks, and fish spears. It was also used by some of these groups to bind arrowheads onto shafts. It was watertight, resistant to decay, and made a smooth union. It was glued on, then tied and sealed with pitch. Often several layers were applied. The Lower Lillooet used a combination of lodgepole pine pitch boiled with bear grease as a glue and sealant. They made strings of twisted cherry bark to tie prongs onto harpoon shafts and as a binding for gaffhooks. The Comox wove fishing weirs from this twine. The Kwakiutl employed the bark to cover and protect wound dressings, sticking it onto the skin with pitch. The Squamish made cherry bark deer calls. In areas where the tree did not occur naturally, the bark was often imported from neighbouring locations; for example, the Manhousat Nootka obtained it from the Gold River area on Vancouver Island.

Cherry wood was considered by the Saanich, at least, to be an excellent fuel; they sometimes used it for the hearth and drill in making friction fires. The wood of the closely related chokecherry (*P. virginiana* L.) was occasionally used by the Okanagan for carving darts, used in a throwing game, and for other small items. The Thompson made root-digger handles from it, and used shredded chokecherry bark woven under the coils of the rims of baskets as ornamentation. The Shuswap used chokecherry wood for salmon stretchers and mixed the fruits with bear grease to make a paint for colouring pictographs. The Blackfoot of Alberta used the wood for incense tongs and roasting skewers because it did not burn easily.

Chokecherry (*Prunus virginiana*).

—Nancy J. Turner

The bark of yet another wild cherry, *P. pensylvanica* L., the pincherry, may have been used by the Shuswap, Carrier, and some of the other groups of the central Interior, in the same manner as bitter cherry bark.

Greasewood	*Purshia tridentata* (Pursh) DC.
(Rose Family)	(Rosaceae)

OTHER NAMES—Antelope bush, bitter brush.

BOTANICAL DESCRIPTION—An erect, gangly, deciduous shrub usually 1–2 m (about 3–6 ft) high with dark grey to blackish bark. The leaves are small and wedge-shaped, deeply 3-toothed at the tip, greenish on the upper surface, greyish beneath. The flowers are yellow and fairly small, but numerous and scattered along the branches, giving the bushes an overall yellowish cast during flower-

Greasewood (*Purshia tridentata*).

—Nancy J. Turner

ing season, which is late spring. The fruits are small, dark, spindle-shaped achenes.

HABITAT—Arid plains to dry, open woods and slopes, usually in association with big sagebrush.

DISTRIBUTION IN BRITISH COLUMBIA—Restricted to the warm dry areas in the southernmost part of the Province—in the Okanagan Valley and the Rocky Mountain Trench.

INDIAN USE—The pitchy quality of the wood makes it a good fuel for producing a hot fire quickly. The Okanagan used it for this purpose, breaking off the branches at ground level and tying them in bundles for burning. They were especially useful during camping trips and in the winter. The Sanpoil-Nespelem Okanagan of Washington used the bark fibre for weaving bags, garments, and soft baskets. It is said that deer like to browse this bush; you can smell it in their meat when they have been eating it. Okanagan children were warned not to play around greasewood bushes because they have many wood ticks. The Okanagan considered the bush to be a type of sagebrush, although it is botanically unrelated. One ethnographer, A. E. Chamberlain, reported that the Kootenay obtained a reddish dye from the fruits.

| **Wild Crabapple** | *Pyrus fusca* **Raf.** |
| (**Rose Family**) | (**Rosaceae**) |

OTHER NAMES—Pacific crabapple, western crabapple, Oregon crabapple.

BOTANICAL DESCRIPTION—A small, straggly tree, sometimes shrub-like, 3–8 m (10–26 ft) high, with rough, grey bark on the trunk. The leaves, deep green, 4–10 cm (1.5–4.0 in.) long, are similar in shape to orchard apple leaves, but often have a prominent, pointed lobe along one or both edges. The flowers are white to pinkish, smaller than orchard apple blossoms, and in flattened clusters of 5–12. The "apples," in long-stemmed, hanging clusters, are small, elongated, yellow to purplish-red when ripe, and very tart. After a frost they turn brown and soft. (Other names are *P. diversifolia* Bong. and *Malus fusca* Schneider.)

Wild crabapple (*Pyrus fusca*).

—Robert D. Turner

HABITAT—Moist woods, stream banks, swamps, and bogs, often in dense thickets.

DISTRIBUTION IN BRITISH COLUMBIA — West of the Coastal mountains, from Vancouver Island to Alaska, up to 800 m (2,500 ft) elevation.

INDIAN USE—The wood is hard and resilient. It was used by Coastal peoples such as the Kwakiutl, Straits Salish, and Halko-melem to make implement handles, bows, wedges, digging sticks, and smaller items, such as gambling sticks and halibut hooks. The Kwakiutl treated the wood by scorching it over an open fire, then boiling it. The Saanich sometimes made fishing floats from it. The Squamish used it in recent times to make axe and sledge-hammer handles and wedges. The Niska made pegs to hold their house boards in place from seasoned crabapple wood soaked in oil. In Washington, the Quileute made maul handles, seal spear prongs, and sea bass lures from crabapple.

Wild Rose   *Rose acicularis* **Lindl.,** *R. gymnocarpa*
                                 Nutt., *R. nutkana* **Presl., and**
                                 R. woodsii **Lindl.**

(Rose Family)   **(Rosaceae)**

OTHER NAMES—These are known variously as prickly rose, dwarf wild rose, common or Nootka rose, and wood rose.

BOTANICAL DESCRIPTION—All are erect shrubs with spiny or thorny stems and pinnately, compound leaves, with usually 5–7 toothed leaflets, similar to those of garden roses, but smaller. The flowers are pale to bright pink, 5-petalled, with yellow centres and numerous stamens. The fruits or "hips" are bright red-orange, consisting of a fleshy rind enclosing many whitish seeds. Hard at first, the rind softens after the first frost. *R. acicularis* has elongated fruits and numerous small spines on the stems and twigs; *R. gymnocarpa* has small flowers, small fruits without persisting sepals, and usually densely bristled stems; *R. nutkana* has large flowers

Wild rose (*Rosa nutkana*).

—Robert D. Turner

244

and fruits and one or two large, flattened thorns at each node, but no small thin spines; and *R. woodsii* has smaller, straight thorns, smaller clustered flowers, and relatively small, round fruits.

HABITAT—*R. acicularis* is found in open woods and hillsides; *R. gymnocarpa* grows in shaded woods; *R. nutkana* is common along roadsides, in thickets, and open woods; and *R. woodsii* is found in open woods and prairies to moist meadows and creeksides.

DISTRIBUTION IN BRITISH COLUMBIA—*R. acicularis* occurs throughout the Interior of the Province; *R. gymnocarpa* is found on both sides of the Cascade Mountains from about 52°N latitude southward; *R. nutkana* is widespread along the Coast and throughout the Interior, south of 56°N latitude; and *R. woodsii* is common throughout the dry parts of the Interior south of 56°N latitude, and in the Peace River District.

INDIAN USE—The wild roses were not as essential in native technology as some other plants, but they were put to a variety of uses in different Indian cultures. The Cowichan, a Halkomelem group, peeled and boiled the roots of the common wild rose *(R. nutkana)* and wove them together with boiled wild gooseberry roots and red cedar roots to make reefnets. The Shuswap made arrows of rose wood (probably *R. acicularis*) and hollowed the stems to make pipe stems. The Thompson used the wood of the dwarf wild rose *(R. gymnocarpa)* to make arrows, handles, and baby carrier hoops. The Okanagan used wild rose leaves to place over and under food in cooking baskets, steaming pits and pots to flavour it and prevent it from burning. They sometimes made fishing lures by tying ant larvae onto a rose flower with horsehair. The Sechelt squeezed wild rose flowers to obtain a perfume. In pre-European times, rose hips were strung to make necklaces by such diverse groups as the Straits Salish of Vancouver Island and the Blackfoot of Alberta.

**Wild Raspberry
and Blackcap**

(Rose Family)

Rubus idaeus L. and
R. leucodermis Dougl.

(Rosaceae)

OTHER NAMES—Blackcap is also known as black raspberry, "blackberry," and "wild loganberry."

BOTANICAL DESCRIPTION — Erect, prickly, deciduous shrubs similar in appearance to cultivated raspberry. Wild raspberry usually has short branches and brownish bark; blackcap branches

Blackcap (*Rubus leucodermis*).

—Nancy J. Turner

are long and arching, and the bark has a bluish-grey appearance. The leaves are prickly-veined beneath and compound, with three (sometimes five in the wild raspberry) sharply pointed leaflets, the terminal one largest, as in garden raspberry leaves. The flowers are white, in small clusters, and the fruits resemble those of garden raspberries, being bright red in the wild raspberry, dark purplish-black in the blackcap. They fall off readily when ripe, and have a sweet, juicy flavour.

HABITAT—Wild raspberry is found along stream banks, in open woods and clearings, and on talus slopes; blackcap grows in open woods, burns, and clearings.

DISTRIBUTION IN BRITISH COLUMBIA—Wild raspberry is widespread in the Interior of the Province, extending to the Coast along some of the northern river valleys; blackcap occurs throughout the southern part of the Province, generally south of 51°N latitude.

INDIAN USE—The berries of both species were squeezed and the juice used as a red stain for wood and other materials by the Thompson and Lillooet.

Thimbleberry   *Rubus parviflorus* **Nutt.**

(Rose Family)   **(Rosaceae)**

BOTANICAL DESCRIPTION—An erect, many-stemmed, unarmed shrub, 0.5–1.5 m (1.5–5 ft) high. The bark is light brown, thin, and shredding. The leaves are large, light green, and resemble maple leaves, with five pointed lobes. They are marginally toothed and finely fuzzy on both sides. The flowers are large and white, in few- to many-flowered, terminal clusters. The fruits are bright red when ripe. They are shallowly cup-shaped and fall loose from their stems easily when ripe. Their taste varies with locality and weather conditions, but ideally they are sweet and flavourful, though somewhat seedy.

HABITAT—Open woods, clearings, and along roadsides, often forming dense thickets.

Thimbleberry (*Rubus parviflorus*).

—Robert D. Turner

DISTRIBUTION IN BRITISH COLUMBIA—Widespread in the lower two-thirds of the Province, south of latitude 55°N; common along the Coast north to the Queen Charlotte Islands.

INDIAN USE—The large, maple-like leaves were used by the Okanagan to line steam-cooking pits, and by the Shuswap and Carrier to cover baskets of berries, to separate different kinds of berries in the same basket, and for drying berries on. Sometimes a makeshift berry-picking container was made by pinning the terminal lobes of a leaf together with a stick to produce a small cup. In Washington, the Quileute used the leaves to wrap cooked elderberries for storage, and the Quinault used them, along with skunk cabbage leaves, to line elderberry preserving baskets. The Cowlitz boiled the bark and used it as soap. The berries were sometimes used as a stain; the Blackfoot of Alberta dyed tanned robes with them and applied them to arrow quivers to colour and straighten them.

Salmonberry	*Rubus spectabilis* Pursh
(Rose Family)	(Rosaceae)

BOTANICAL DESCRIPTION—A tall, raspberry-like shrub with reddish-brown bark and numerous short prickles along the stems. The leaves, like those of raspberry, are compound, with two lateral leaflets and one larger terminal one. The flowers, usually solitary, bloom early in the spring before the leaves have fully expanded. They are pink and fairly showy. The berries resemble large raspberries. They are found in two colour forms—salmon or "gold" and deep red or "ruby." These grow on different bushes but can both be found in the same locality.

HABITAT—Shaded swamps, damp woods, and moist clearings, often forming dense thickets.

DISTRIBUTION IN BRITISH COLUMBIA—Abundant along the Coast, west of the Coastal mountains, from Vancouver Island to Alaska.

INDIAN USE—The long, straight, woody shoots were used by the Kwakiutl and Haida as spears in throwing games. The Kwak-

249

Salmonberry (*Rubus spectabilis*).

—Robert D. Turner

iutl sometimes used them for arrow shafts and the Haida used them to keep sheets of cedar-bark roofing flat by driving the sticks crosswise at intervals through the inner layers of the bark. The Squamish used short hollowed pieces of salmonberry stem as the valves between harpoon heads and foreshafts and as the socket between the hook and handle of a gaffhook. The Comox sometimes used a tube of the hollowed stem to pour water into a covered steam-cooking pit. The Makah of Washington made pipe stems from the hollowed stems and the Quileute used them to make plugs for hair seal skin floats.

Hardhack
(**Rose Family**)

Spiraea douglasii **Hook.**
(**Rosaceae**)

OTHER NAMES—Douglas spiraea, steeplebush.

BOTANICAL DESCRIPTION—An erect, wiry, deciduous shrub with reddish-brown bark and oblong, elliptic to oval leaves, usually

Hardhack (*Spiraea douglasii*).

—Robert D. Turner

251

4–10 cm (1.6–4.0 in.) long, dark green above, pale green beneath, and toothed around the upper half. The flowers are small, pink to rose, and numerous, in dense, elongated, terminal clusters. The fruiting heads are deep brown, remaining on the bushes over the winter.

HABITAT—Stream banks, lake margins, bogs, swamps, and damp meadows from sea level to subalpine elevations, often forming dense thickets.

DISTRIBUTION IN BRITISH COLUMBIA—Along the Coast and in parts of the Interior south from about 56°N latitude.

INDIAN USE—The wiry, branching twigs were used by the Nootka to make implements for gathering tubular dentalium (*Dentalium pretiosum* Sowerby) shells from the mud-bottomed bays of the west coast of Vancouver Island. These shells, also called money tusk or wampum, were a valuable form of currency throughout the Northwest in the days before the White traders. The Nootkan peoples were virtually the sole suppliers of dentalia in the North Pacific area. Long strings or wallet-sized packets of the shells, all meticulously sorted by size, were traded from group to group as far east as the Great Plains. The implement for collecting them consisted of a broom-like bundle of hardhack twigs or hardwood splints tied to a pole of red cedar or some other wood. A weighted board with a hole in the centre just big enough to slip partway down the bundle of twigs was placed over the pole, and more poles could be added on depending on the depth of the dentalia beds. The shell gatherer took this implement out to the beds by canoe and lowered it into the water until it was nearly touching the bottom. Then he pushed down hard into the mud, causing the twigs or splints to spread slightly, then close as the weighted board settled over them. With luck, the gatherer would find one or two dentalia entrapped in the twigs when he pulled the implement up. In a rich area he could gather large quantities of the molluscs in a relatively short period of time. These he would clean and sort in preparation for a lucrative trade.

The Bella Coola used hardhack branches to make hooks for drying and smoking salmon. The Vancouver Island Salish made blades, halibut hooks, and cambium scrapers from the fire-hardened wood, and the Lummi of Washington used it to make salmon spreaders and roasting sticks.

Black Cottonwood	*Populus balsamifera* **L. ssp.**
and Balsam Poplar	*trichocarpa* **(T. & G.) Brayshaw**
	and *P. balsamifera* **L. ssp.** *balsamifera*

(Willow Family)   **(Salicaceae)**

OTHER NAME—Both are known simply as poplar.

BOTANICAL DESCRIPTION—These are rough-barked, deciduous trees, up to 40 m (130 ft) tall, with resinous, sweet-smelling, spring buds and leaves. The leaves are long-stemmed and narrowly to broadly oval-shaped, with heart-shaped to wedge-shaped bases, pointed tips, and finely toothed margins. In spring the leaves are yellow-green, maturing to dark green above and pale green beneath. They turn golden-yellow in autumn and become black soon after dropping. The flowers are long, hanging catkins, the male and female being on separate trees. At fruiting times the female catkins are covered with soft, downy "cotton," which is released with the seeds in mid-summer, filling the air with bits of white fluff resembling snowflakes.

These subspecies are treated by some botanists as separate species (*P. trichocarpa* T. & G. and *P. balsamifera* L.), but they freely intergrade and the distinctions between them are inconstant and difficult to determine. The distinguishing characters are as follows: the male catkins of ssp. *trichocarpa* usually have 30 to 60 stamens while those of ssp. *balsamifera* usually have 20 or fewer; the fruits of ssp. *trichocarpa* are hairy, spherical, and 3-valved, while those of ssp. *balsamifera* are smooth, ovoid, and 2-valved; the young shoots of ssp. *trichocarpa* are often angled, while those of ssp. *balsamifera* are rounded. *Populus balsamifera* was known for many years as *P. tacamahaca* Mill., with the common name of tacamahac or hackmatack.

HABITAT—Both species are found along watercourses, gullies and alluvial plains; they are able to withstand periodic flooding.

Black cottonwood (*Populus balsamifera* ssp. *trichocarpa*).
—Robert D. Turner

DISTRIBUTION IN BRITISH COLUMBIA—Black cottonwood occurs generally in the western part of the Province and in the south, while balsam poplar is more common in the central Interior, extending northward and eastward. Neither is found on the Queen Charlotte Islands.

INDIAN USE—These trees are seldom distinguished by native peoples, and are discussed here as one. The wood is light brown, soft, moderately strong, straight-grained, of uniform texture, and easily worked, but not very durable. It was used by many native groups, including the Okanagan, Shuswap, Carrier, Tahltan, Niska, Upper Stalo, and occasionally the Vancouver Island Salish, to make dugout canoes. These were smaller and lighter than the red-cedar dugouts commonly used on the Coast. They could not be widened by steaming, were not as durable, and tended to become waterlogged, but they served well on the lakes and rivers of the Interior, where large cedars were not available. Additionally, the Thompson and Okanagan used cottonwood to carve sideboards for riding and pack saddles, the Okanagan used cottonwood boards in cradles to flatten their children's heads and cottonwood poles to make fishing weirs. The Niska sometimes used the wood to carve masks.

Cottonwood was considered an excellent fuel. The Okanagan and Shuswap used it, fresh or partially rotten, for smoking buckskin. The Lillooet and Tahltan used it for smoking fish, but a Shuswap informant maintained that it was too strong and would make the fish bitter. The Kootenay used dead, dried cottonwood to bank a fire overnight. Lengths of cottonwood root, dried for a long time, were used by the Thompson, Upper Stalo, and others to make fire drills and hearths for friction fires. The Okanagan used dried cottonwood tops for the drills and dead cottonwood roots for the hearths.

Cottonwood ashes were used by the Okanagan as a soap substitute, for cleaning buckskin clothing and washing the hair, and by the Shuswap for laundering clothes. The Shuswap put the ashes in a can of water and let them sit overnight. The upper layer of liquid was poured off into another container, strained, and bottled. A small quantity of the fluid, placed in the laundry was said to act like lye. The Thompson used the inner part of the bark as soap. The bark was stripped off when young and green, the outer part scraped off and discarded, and the white inner portion dried, and packaged into small, fist-sized bundles, which could be stored for winter use. Within the last 100 years or so, individuals carried their own soap bundles with them wherever they went. It was said that the Hudson's Bay Company mixed cottonwood inner bark with tallow to make soap, and some Thompson people used it for laundry soap during World War II.

Large sheets of the bark, which on mature trees is thick and corky, were stripped off standing trees by the Okanagan, Lillooet, and some Coast Salish groups and made into rectangular containers or "buckets" for carrying and storing food. The Okanagan also used the bark to line and cover underground food storage pits, protecting the food against "gophers" and other burrowing rodents. The Niska sometimes built temporary cabins from cottonwood bark. They also split the roots and twisted them into ropes for binding and tying fish traps and house planks.

The aromatic gum from the spring buds was used as a glue by the Okanagan, Lillooet, and Shuswap. The buds were harvested from the branches, or the bud scales were gathered after they had fallen to the ground. They were heated and squeezed to extract the gum, said to be the strongest cement known in the early days— stronger even than fish slime glue. The Lillooet and Shuswap used it to stick down the sinew binding feathers onto arrow shafts. The Okanagan employed it for gluing on arrowheads, spearheads, and fish hooks, and for sealing the cracks in birch-bark canoes. The Coast Salish of Vancouver Island also used it to waterproof baskets and boxes.

The Okanagan mixed the gum, which is a rich yellow colour, with various pigments, such as alder bark, larch, wolf lichen, and charcoal, to make paint. For this purpose, the buds were picked from the trees, sliced, and boiled in grease. The fluffy "cotton" from the fruiting catkins was sometimes used by the Thompson and Lillooet for stuffing pillows and mattresses, although it was hard to obtain in quantity.

Trembling Aspen   *Populus tremuloides* **Michx.**

(Willow Family)   **(Salicaceae)**

OTHER NAMES—Aspen poplar, white poplar.

BOTANICAL DESCRIPTION—A slender, medium-sized, deciduous tree up to 25 m (about 80 ft) tall, with few branches on the lower trunk. The bark is smooth and light green to whitish. The leaves are broadly oval, rounded at the base, pointed at the tip, and shallowly toothed. The leafstalks are flattened vertically near the blade, allowing the leaves to flutter at the slightest breeze. The leaves turn golden in autumn, making a stand of the trees a spectacular sight. The trees are dioecious; the flowers are borne in hanging catkins, which mature before the leaves expand in the spring. Vegetative reproduction by the growth of suckers from the root system is common.

Trembling aspen (*Populus tremuloides*).

—Nancy J. Turner

HABITAT—Upland slopes, in moist depressions, or on alluvial sites, from near sea level to subalpine elevations.

DISTRIBUTION IN BRITISH COLUMBIA—Particularly abundant in the central and northeastern Interior, where it forms extensive stands; occurs throughout the Interior and sporadically along the Coast, but not on the Queen Charlotte Islands.

INDIAN USE—The wood, nearly white in colour, is soft, brittle, and not very durable, but seasons and works well. The Upper Thompson sometimes used it to make dugout canoes, although it was said to be heavier than the red cedar used by the Lower Thompson and the Coastal peoples. The Okanagan scraped deer hides on aspen logs. They preferred to get them in early May because the bark peels off easily at this time. Shuswap and Blackfoot boys made whistles from the branches, and aspen poles were used by the Shuswap to make tent poles and drying racks for fish and deer meat, but they were said to rot after only a couple of years. The Kootenay made hide-covered saddles from aspen wood. The Shuswap and Blackfoot and probably most other Interior groups used the wood as a fuel. The Carrier used rotten aspen wood for lining babies' cradles; it was soft and absorbent and made a good diaper material.

The Thompson made a cleansing solution for washing guns, traps, and buckskins by boiling aspen branches in water. Hunters and others washed themselves in this liquid to clean their skin and eliminate human odour. The Okanagan used aspen and cottonwood as a weather indicator; if the leaves began to shimmer when there was no perceptible wind, it would soon become stormy.

Willows   *Salix* **Species**

(Willow Family)   **(Salicaceae)**

BOTANICAL DESCRIPTION—These are deciduous shrubs or trees with rounded to elongated leaves. The flowers are borne in catkins, male and female on separate plants. Most willows are wind pollinated and have fluffy fruits which are carried on the wind. There are nearly 50 species of willows in British Columbia. These vary

Pacific willow (*Salix lasiandra*).

—Robert D. Turner

widely in size and habit, bark colour and texture, leaf shape, degree of hairiness, and many other characters. Furthermore, many of them intergrade freely. Among the species used by native peoples are:

S. *lasiandra* Benth., Pacific willow—a narrow-leafed, slender tree up to 12 m (40 ft) tall;

S. *exigua* Nutt., sandbar, "pink-barked," "silver," or coyote willow—a spreading shrub up to 3 m (10 ft) high with long, slender, erect stems, smooth, pinkish-brown bark, and long, narrow leaves which are greyish-green and usually lightly toothed at the margins;

S. *scouleriana* Barratt, Scouler's willow—a large shrub or small tree with smooth, grey bark and oblong "mouse-ear" leaves which taper at the base. The undersides of the leaves are often covered with rust-coloured hairs;

S. hookeriana Barratt, Hooker's willow—a large shrub or small tree with oval, woolly, smooth-edged leaves;

S. rigida Muhl., Mackenzie willow—a tall shrub with yellow or brownish bark and finely toothed, lance-shaped leaves; and

S. bebbiana Sarg., Bebb's willow—a tall shrub or small tree with grey-brown bark and oblong oval to lance-shaped leaves, whitish and usually thinly hairy beneath.

Many other species were used but most were not distinguished as separate types by native peoples or ethnographers and are therefore treated only in a general context. Where the species used is known, it is mentioned.

HABITAT—Most willows occur in moist sites—in swamps and along watercourses. All of the species mentioned grow in wet ground. Sandbar willow forms dense colonies on sand and gravel bars along rivers and streams. Scouler's willow grows on upland slopes and in moderately dry woods as well as moist draws. Bebb's willow also grows in upland sites.

DISTRIBUTION IN BRITISH COLUMBIA — Willows are found throughout the Province, from sea level to alpine elevations. Of the individual species mentioned, Pacific willow grows in suitable habitats throughout the Province; sandbar willow is widespread in the Interior east of the Coastal mountain ranges; Scouler's willow occurs throughout, but is especially common along the southern Coast; Hooker's willow is restricted to the Coastal regions, mainly in the south; Mackenzie willow grows throughout, especially in the eastern part; and Bebb's willow occurs throughout the Interior east of the Coast and Cascade Mountains.

INDIAN USE—The Fraser River Lillooet called Pacific willow the "match plant." They dried the wood and used it for both the hearth and the drill in making friction fires. They used dry grass and big sagebrush bark as tinder. The Cowlitz of Washington also used this species to make fire drills. Some Lillooet groups used a willow fire to burn diatomaceous earth into a fine white powder for treating wool. The Okanagan used the wood of Bebb's willow,

Scouler's willow (*Salix scouleriana*).

—Robert D. Turner

Scouler's willow, and others to make hide-stretchers, barbecue sticks, and fish traps, and used the twigs for smoking hides when a white colouring was desired. They used willow twigs daily to clean the teeth. The Shuswap used the wood of the previously mentioned species for smoking salmon, drying meat and fish, and for making barbecue sticks and fishing weirs. They used rotten willow roots as punk, which could be ignited and carried while travelling. The Kootenay considered willow wood an excellent fuel for smoking meat. The Flathead of Montana and the Blackfoot of Alberta made sweathouses from willow branches, the last group specifically from sandbar willow. The Tahltan used willow for smoking fish and for making gambling sticks and snowshoes. The Sekani made small bows from sandbar willow. The Carrier made berry drying racks, packboards, and snowshoe cross-sticks from willow wood. For snowshoes, willow was said to be light but not very durable.

The Haida made spoons and other small articles and frames for summer houses from Scouler's willow, and the Kwakiutl made willow knitting needles and game hoops. The Vancouver Island Salish sometimes made bows from willow wood. The Quileute of Washington used the branches of young Hooker's willows as poles for fish weirs because they were said to take root wherever they were "planted" in the river.

The supple, flexible nature of willow branches and bark, especially of some species, made them extremely useful as cordage, for lines, nets, and ropes, and for binding and tying. The Straits Salish and Halkomelem of Vancouver Island and the adjacent Mainland peeled the bark of Hooker's willow and other species in May or June, removed the outer part, split the inner tissue into thin strands, and twisted these together into a long rope. This was used to make fishing lines and various types of nets, including gill-nets, reef-nets, purse-nets, bag-nets, and even duck-nets. They also used the bark for basket imbrication.

The Snohomish and Quinault of Washington made tumplines, slings, and harpoon lines from Hooker's willow bark. The Klallam made string from the bark of the Sitka willow (*S. sitchensis* Bong.) and the Chehalis used the inner part of Pacific willow to make a two-ply string. The Lower Lillooet also made twine, for tying fish traps, from Pacific willow bark, and made strong ropes by braiding the bark and twigs together. They used these as anchor lines and for attaching cedar-wood floats to nets. Some Lillooet people, reportedly only the poorer ones, shredded the inner bark of willow and wove it into robes, skirts, bodices, aprons, and socks. Sandbar willow, called literally "rope plant" by the Lillooet, was the most commonly used species for making rope. The branches, bark and all, were twisted into rope while still green, remaining pliable even when dry.

Willow bark was used by the Thompson, as by the Lillooet, to weave bags, mats, capes, aprons, and fibre blankets. The Thompson, however, were said to use only the bark from dead trees. Sandbar willow withes were used for construction by the Thompson, and the bark was woven into saddle blankets. The Okanagan twisted the bark of Bebb's, sandbar, and other willows into cord for tying rafts and fish traps together and for weaving bags, dresses, and skirts. In making a woman's skirt, willow was stretched while

Sam Mitchell of Lillooet, British Columbia, twisting a branch of sandbar willow to make a rope.

—Adrianne Aiken

still green, hung up to dry for a day, then softened by rubbing a stone scraper across it many times. The inner bark was shredded into a cotton-like substance and used for diapers, wound dressings, and sanitary napkins for women. Sandbar willow branches were used by the Okanagan for laying fish on, and willow leaves were used for wrapping and serving fish.

The Shuswap used withes of Scouler's willow and others for sewing birch-bark canoes, and for making cradle rims and hoops.

Hooker's willow (*Salix hookeriana*).

—Robert D. Turner

They used the inner bark to make headbands and strips of the bark to string edible roots for drying. They also used strips of bark for lashing and tying. The Carrier made fish nets of sandbar willow bark and the Tahltan used the bark and twigs for tying house walls together. The Kootenay twisted the green bark of the sandbar willow and other species and used it for lashing objects such as rafts. The Flathead used the bark of one species of willow to make ropes and bridles and for weaving baskets.

Some groups, such as the Haida, used the spring catkins, or "pussy willows" of certain species of willow as decoration, at least in recent years. The Straits Salish sometimes used willow bark to make a grey dye for colouring mountain goat wool.

Stinging Nettle

(Nettle Family)

Urtica dioica L.

(Urticaceae)

OTHER NAMES—"Indian spinach," Northwest nettle.

BOTANICAL DESCRIPTION—An herbaceous perennial, 1–3 m (3–10 ft) tall, with spreading rhizomes. The ragged-looking leaves are borne in opposite pairs along the stem. They are 7–15 cm (3–6 in.) long, on short stalks, rounded at the base, broadest below the middle, and tapering to a sharp point. The edges are sharply toothed. The flowers are greenish and inconspicuous, clustered in drooping bunches at the stem nodes. The leaves and stems are covered with stiff hairs which cause stinging and blistering when touched. Another name is *U. lyallii* Wats.

HABITAT—Usually growing in large patches at the edges of clearings and old fields, also in damp roadside thickets and shaded woods.

DISTRIBUTION IN BRITISH COLUMBIA—Common along the Coast from Vancouver Island to Alaska, and in the southern Interior.

INDIAN USE—Nettle was an important source of fibre for most Coastal peoples, including the Straits Salish, Halkomelem, virtually all the western Washington groups, the Squamish, Kwakiutl, Nootka,

Stinging nettle (*Urtica dioica*).

—Nancy J. Turner

Bella Coola, Tsimshian, Haida, and Tlingit, as well as the Niska, Gitksan, Carrier, Lower Lillooet, and Lower Thompson. The Interior Salish people preferred to use Indian hemp fibre. Nettle stems were gathered in the fall, usually in October, after the plants had completely matured and were beginning to die. The Bella Coola harvested them when the first snow hit the mountain tops.

The leaves were stripped off and the stems dried in the sun for several days. The Vancouver Island Salish also dried them over a fire. The thin outer skin was cracked off and the outer fibres separated from the inner pith and spun on the bare thigh or with a wooden disk spindle, often of broad-leafed maple wood. The individual strands were spliced together by rolling or twisting. The resulting thread was twisted into a two- or four-ply twine. This was used for tying and binding and for making tumplines, snares, harpoon and fishing lines, fishing nets, duck-nets, and even deer-nets. In the Bella Coola culture, the men made the fishing nets, although as everywhere, the women prepared the twine. Nettle fishing nets were often dyed brown with alder bark to make them invisible to fish under the water.

The Saanich of Vancouver Island formerly spun nettle fibre with bird down to make blankets and sleeping bags in the days before mountain goat wool could be easily obtained from the Mainland. The Cowichan used nettle fibre for tattooing lines under the skin, as a form of personal adornment. They rubbed pigment on a nettle thread and ran it beneath the skin with a fine hardwood needle.

Stinging nettle fibre (Nootka) (#2267, Ethnology Division, British Columbia Provincial Museum, Victoria).

—Robert D. Turner

The Tlingit of Alaska made a red dye by boiling nettle stems and leaves in urine. The Okanagan poisoned arrows by boiling them in water with nettle roots. According to Squamish lore, when stinging nettle shoots were first coming out of the ground in the spring it was a sign that the seals were having their young.

APPENDIX

FLOWERING PLANTS OF MINOR IMPORTANCE IN THE TECHNOLOGIES OF BRITISH COLUMBIA INDIANS AND THEIR NEIGHBOURS

(These plants are listed alphabetically by their genus names within their families, which appear in alphabetical order within the major categories of Monocotyledons and Dicotyledons.)

MONOCOTYLEDONS

Sedge Family (Cyperaceae)

Spike rush [*Eleocharis palustris* (L.) R. & S.]—The Okanagan used the stems for bedding and for sitting on in the sweathouse.

Rush Family (Juncaceae)

Rush (*Juncus balticus* Willd.)—The Blackfoot Indians of Alberta obtained a brown dye, which shaded into green, from the stems of this plant.

Common rush (*Juncus effusus* L.)—The stems were sometimes used for weaving by the Mainland Comox; the Quinault of Washington used them to weave tumplines and, mixed with cat-tail, as string. The Snuqualmi used them for tying things.

Lily Family (Liliaceae)

Nodding onion (*Allium cernuum* Roth.)—The Vancouver Island Salish rubbed the bulbs on their skin to repel mosquitoes and other insects.

Queenscup [*Clintonia uniflora* (Schult.) Kunth]. The Thompson mashed the fruits and used them as a blue dye, but large quantities had to be used to make it effective.

Twisted stalk and its relatives [*Streptopus amplexifolius* (L.) DC., *Smilacina racemosa* (L.) Desf., and *Smilacina stellata* (L.) Desf.]—The Thompson and Shuswap used the roots or the whole plants of these species as a scent. They were tied to the body or on the clothes or hair. If the spring salmon catch was poor, a Lower Lillooet fisherman would rinse his gill-net in a solution of boiled twisted stalk.

Indian hellebore (*Veratrum viride* Ait.)—James Teit reports that the Lillooet used the stem fibre of this poisonous plant for weaving wallets, bags, and pouches.

Death camas (*Zygadenus venenosus* S. Wats.)—The Okanagan used the mashed bulbs as an arrow poison.

Bur-reed Family (Sparganiaceae)

Bur-reed (*Sparganium eurycarpum* Engelm.)—In recent years the Okanagan have used this plant as hay for their cattle.

Common rush (*Juncus effusus*).

—Robert D. Turner

DICOTYLEDONS

Sumac Family (Anacardiaceae)

Smooth sumac *(Rhus glabra* L.)—The Thompson experimented with the fruits as a source of red dye but the results were not satisfactory. When the leaves change colour in the fall the Okanagan know that the sockeye salmon are turning red also.

Celery Family (Apiaceae or Umbelliferae)

Angelica *(Angelica genuflexa* Nutt.)—Kootenay children made whistles and blowguns from the hollow stems, but they had to be careful not to confuse them with those of the water hemlock [*Cicuta douglasii* (DC.) Coult. & Rose], which are very poisonous. The Bella Coola used the stems as breathing tubes when hiding under water in times of danger. Makah and Quileute children of Washington made whistles out of the related water parsnip *(Oenanthe sarmentosa* Presl. ex DC.).

Water hemlock [*Cicuta douglasii* (DC.) Coult. & Rose]—The Okanagan used the powdered root as an arrow poison.

Birthwort Family (Aristolochiaceae)

Wild Ginger *(Asarum caudatum* Lindl.)—The Thompson and Okanagan sometimes used this plant, mixed with *Sphagnum* moss, as a bedding for infants. It was valued for its pleasant scent.

Wild ginger *(Asarum caudatum).*

—Nancy J. Turner

271

Aster Family (Asteraceae or Compositae)

Yarrow (*Achillea millefolium* L.)—The Haida used the stems to string butter clams on for drying; the clams were then eaten right off the stems. They imparted a pleasant taste to the food. The Okanagan placed the leaves on hot coals to make a smudge for repelling mosquitos. The Flathead of Montana rubbed the flower heads in the armpits as a deodorant.

Pearly everlasting [*Anaphalis margaritacea* (L.) B. & H.]—The Thompson used the dried flower heads for stuffing pillows.

Fleabane [*Erigeron peregrinus* (Pursh) Greene] originally listed as *E. salsuginosus* (Hook.) A. Gray—The Thompson name means "star flower," according to James Teit. The heads were used as a pattern in basketry; they were said to be easier to duplicate than other plants.

Pineapple weed [*Matricaria matricarioides* (Less.) Porter]—Kootenay children used to thread the flower heads for beads. Adults hung it in the house because of its nice smell, and used it to stuff pillows. The Flathead of Montana used it as an insect repellent. The whole plants were placed in alternate layers in parfleches (skin bags) with meat or berries to keep the bugs off, and the leaves were dried and sprinkled over fresh meat and fruit for the same purpose.

Coltsfoot [*Petasites frigidus* (L.) Fries]—The Quinault of Washington used the leaves to cover berries in steam-cooking pits.

Goldenrod (*Solidago canadensis* L.)—Okanagan children used to play with the plants, pulling them up and using them as whips.

Honeysuckle Family (Caprifoliaceae)

Highbush cranberry [*Viburnum edule* (Michx.) Raf.]—The Kootenay made pipe stems from the hollowed out branches.

Boxwood Family (Celastraceae)

False box [*Pachystima myrsinites* (Pursh) Raf.]—Saanich women gathered the branches in recent years and sold them to local florists.

Goosefoot Family (Chenopodiaceae)

Lamb's quarters or pigweed (*Chenopodium album* L.)—The Blackfoot of Alberta obtained a green dye from the young shoots.

Jerusalem oak (*Chenopodium botrys* L.)—This is a common Eurasian weed but, according to James Teit and Elsie Steedman, it was used in large quantities by the Thompson as a scent. It was wound in necklaces, stuffed in pillows, bags, pouches, and baskets, and tied in the clothes and hair or worn in little skin bags next to the skin.

Strawberry blite [*Chenopodium capitatum* (L.) Asch.; originally known as *Blitum capitatum* L.]—The Thompson and Carrier made a red stain from the fruits by crushing them. The Thompson used it to colour the face and body, as well as clothes, skins, and wood. The Carrier sometimes coloured spruce roots with it.

Bindweed Family (Convolvulariaceae)

Field bindweed (*Convolvulus arvensis* L.)—This is an introduced weed. In recent years Okanagan hunters used the stems as a packrope for carrying birds and marmots home after hunting.

Heather Family (Ericaceae)

Kinnikinnick [*Arctostaphylos uva-ursi* (L.) Spreng.]—The Lillooet sometimes used the roots to make temporary pipes. The Blackfoot of Alberta used the dried berries in their rattles and strung them on necklaces.

Salal (*Gaultheria shallon* Pursh)—The Saanich and other Vancouver Island Salish groups placed the branches in their steam-cooking pits, over and under food such as camas bulbs. The Nootka made a purple dye from the berries. The Kwakiutl mixed them with black twinberry fruits to intensify the colour. They and the Squamish used the branches to whip soapberries.

False azalea (*Menziesia ferruginea* Smith)—The Quileute of Washington wove the twigs with cedar bark to make a grill for sitting on in the bottom of a canoe.

Pinedrops (*Pterospora andromedea* Nutt.)—The Flathead of Montana boiled this plant with blue clematis to make a shampoo.

White rhododendron (*Rhododendron albiflorum* Hook.)—The Thompson used this plant as a scent.

Blue huckleberries (*Vaccinium membranaceum* Dougl. ex Hook. and other *Vaccinium* species)—The Okanagan, Lillooet, and Tlingit of Alaska mashed the berries to obtain a purple dye for basket materials.

Pea Family (Fabaceae or Leguminosae)

Locoweed (*Astragalus miser* Dougl.)—The Okanagan used the plants to wipe the turpentine-like juice from the inside of lodgepole pine bark when the cambium was being harvested.

Sea pea (*Lathyrus japonicus* Willd.)—The Manhousat Nootka placed the sweet-smelling flowers in their small grass baskets to scent them and make them sell better.

Lupine (*Lupinus sericeus* Pursh and other *Lupinus* species)—The Okanagan used these flowers as bedding and flooring in the sweathouse. Lupine was considered the marmot's favourite food. When it bloomed in spring it was a sign to the Okanagan that the marmots were fat enough to eat.

Giant vetch (*Vicia gigantea* Hook.)—The Makah of Washington used the leaves and vines to cover sprouts while steaming.

Garry oak (*Quercus garryana*).

—Nancy J. Turner

274

Beech Family (Fagaceae)

Garry Oak (*Quercus garryana* Dougl.)—The Cowlitz of Washington used the wood to make combs and digging sticks, and as a fuel.

Gooseberry Family (Grossulariaceae)

Stink currant (*Ribes bracteosum* Dougl.)—The Quileute of Washington used the hollowed stems to inflate seal paunches used as oil containers. They used the leaves to line and cover elderberry storage containers of hemlock bark.

Mint Family (Lamiaceae or Labiatae)

Canada mint (*Mentha arvensis* L.)—The Thompson, Shuswap, and the Flathead of Montana used this plant as a scent. The Shuswap placed it under pillows and kept it around the house "just for the smell of it." The Flathead put the plants in the corners of houses, on the floors of sweathouses, and kept it in suitcases and around the house to keep insects away. The Blackfoot of Alberta boiled their traps in a mint solution to destroy the human scent.

Bee balm (*Monarda fistulosa* L.)—The Flathead of Montana dried and powdered the leaves and sprinkled them over fresh meat or fruit as an insect repellent. The Kootenay of Montana placed the leaves on rocks in the sweathouse as a perfume.

Coyote mint (*Monardella odoratissima* Benth.)—The Colville and Sanpoil-Nespelem Okanagan of Washington used this plant to wipe spears, harpoons, animal snares, arrows, fishing hooks, and fishing lines to cleanse them and remove the human scent.

Hedge nettle (*Stachys cooleyae* Heller)—The Makah and Quinault of Washington used this plant to cover steaming sprouts.

Phlox Family (Polemoniaceae)

Scarlet gilia [*Gilia aggregata* (Pursh) Spreng.]—The Flathead of Montana dried these plants and placed them in bags to make sachets.

Buckwheat Family (Polygonaceae)

Wild buckwheat (*Eriogonum heracleoides* Nutt. and other *Eriogonum* species)—The stems were used to play a game by Okanagan children. They broke off the main stem, leaving one side-branch attached, to make a hook. Each child took one of these. They hooked them together and pulled. The first one to break his stick lost the game.

Primrose Family (Primulaceae)

Shooting star [*Dodecatheon pauciflorum* (Durand) Greene]—The Okanagan mashed the flowers and smeared them on arrows as a pink stain.

Playing Okanagan game with wild buckwheat (*Eriogonum heracleoides*).

—Robert D. Turner

Buttercup Family (Ranunculaceae)

Wild anemone (*Anemone multifida* Poir.)—The Thompson pounded the seed fluff into "flannel cloth" and used it for baby diapers. They used a strong decoction of the whole plant to kill lice and fleas.

Sagebrush buttercup (*Ranunculus glaberrimus* Hook.)—The Thompson washed the flowers, or whole plants, and rubbed them on arrow points as a poison. Other species of buttercup could be used if *R. glaberrimus* was not available.

Meadow rue (*Thalictrum occidentale* Gray)—The Flathead of Montana dried the seeds, chewed them until pulverized, then rubbed them on the hair and body as a perfume.

Buckthorn Family (Rhamnaceae)

Buckbrush (*Ceanothus sanguineus* Pursh)—The Okanagan used the wood as a fuel for smoking deer meat if other woods were not available. The branches, especially the buds, were said to be an important food for deer in spring.

Snowbrush (*Ceanothus velutinus* Dougl. ex Hook.)—The Shuswap placed the branches on a hot stove to fumigate a house. The smoke acted both as a disinfectant and an insect repellent.

Cascara (*Rhamnus purshiana* DC.). The Manhousat Nootka made chisel handles from the wood. The Skagit of Washington boiled the bark to make a green dye for mountain goat wool.

Rose Family (Rosaceae)

Wild strawberry (*Fragaria* spp.)—Lillooet girls used to wear headbands and belts of strawberry runners plaited together in three or four strands.

Three-flowered avens (*Geum triflorum* Pursh)—The Blackfoot of Alberta crushed the ripe seeds and used them as a perfume.

Ninebark [*Physocarpus capitatus* (Pursh) Kuntze.]—The Cowichan of Vancouver Island recently made knitting needles from the wood, and the Nootka made children's bows and other small items from it.

Mallow ninebark [*Physocarpus malvaceus* (Greene) Kuntze.]—The Southern Okanagan of Washington sometimes made bows from the wood.

Silverweed (*Potentilla anserina* L.).—The Blackfoot of Alberta used the runners as ties for leggings and blankets.

Shrubby cinquefoil (*Potentilla fruticosa* L.). The Blackfoot of Alberta used the dry, flaky bark as tinder for making friction fires.

Trailing wild blackberry (*Rubus ursinus* Cham. & Schlecht.)—The Saanich of Vancouver Island used these vines to place over and under food in steam-cooking pits, and also for ritual scrubbing. They and other Coast Salish groups sometimes used the fruits as a purple stain.

Mountain ash (*Sorbus sitchensis* Roemer)—The Carrier sometimes used the wood to make sidesticks for snowshoes.

Madder Family (Rubiaceae)

Bedstraw (*Galium aparine* L.)—The Cowichan rubbed the plants of this and other species on their hands to remove pitch. They used the dried plants as tinder for lighting fires.

Northern bedstraw (*Galium boreale* L.)—The Blackfoot of Alberta obtained a red dye from the fine roots. If they were boiled too long, the colour changed to yellow.

Sweet-scented bedstraw (*Galium triflorum* Michx.)—The Blackfoot used the dried flowers as a perfume.

Figwort Family (Scrophulariaceae)

Indian paintbrush [*Castilleja miniata* Dougl. ex Hook. and *C. unalaschensis* (Cham. & Schlecht.) Malte. X *miniata*]—Young Bella Coola girls played a game with these flowers. They formed two teams and lined up on opposite sides facing each other. One team had an Indian paintbrush, and chanted the Bella Coola name of the flower. A girl from the other team had to come up and face the singers. If she smiled or laughed, she had to go back, but if she kept a straight face her team got the flower and they sang the song and tried to make a girl from the first team smile. The Kwakiutl used Indian paintbrush in bouquets.

Indian paintbrush (*Castilleja unalaschensis* x *miniata*) used in a
Bella Coola children's game.

—Nancy J. Turner

Owl's clover (*Orthocarpus luteus* Nutt.)—The Blackfoot of Alberta used
to dye small skins with the crushed plants. Plants in full bloom were
crushed and pressed firmly on the skin, imparting a reddish-tan colour.
They were also used to dye horsehair and feathers.

Wood betony (*Pedicularis bracteosa* Benth.)—The leaves were used by
Thompson women as a pattern for basket designs.

Blue penstemon (*Penstemon confertus* Dougl. and *P. pruinosus* Dougl. ex
Lindl.)—The Okanagan boiled the flowers and rubbed them on arrows
and other items to give them a blue colouring, said to be indelible.

Shrubby penstemon [*Penstemon fruticosus* (Pursh) Greene]—The Okanagan mashed the leaves and placed them inside moccasins as padding.
The Lillooet used the leafy branches to rub bunches of nodding onions
before cooking to "get the whiskers off" and give them a better taste.

Valerian Family (Valerianaceae)

Mountain valerian (*Valeriana sitchensis* Bong.)—The Shuswap used this
plant as a perfume and disinfectant. They also used to bathe race
horses with it.

Shrubby penstemon (*Penstemon fruticosus*).

—Nancy J. Turner

GLOSSARY

Achene—a small, dry, one-seeded, closed fruit, such as a dandelion "seed."

Algae (*Alga,* singular)—a large group of plants, mostly aquatic or marine, having no true roots, stems, leaves, or specialized conduction tissue; includes seaweeds.

Alternate—situated singly at each node, as the leaves on a stem.

Annual—a plant that lives only one year or season.

Axil—the angle between a leaf- or flower-stem and the main stem of a plant.

Biennial—a plant that lives only two years; flowers and fruits are usually produced only in the second year.

Blade—the expanded part of a leaf (or petal).

Bract—a modified leaf, either small and scale-like or large and petal-like.

Bryophyte—any member of the plant division Bryophyta, comprising the mosses and liverworts.

Carpel—a simple pistil (female reproductive structure of a flowering plant) or one unit of a compound pistil, bearing the ovules or undeveloped seeds.

Catkin—a drooping, elongated cluster of petalless flowers, either male or female, as on willows, alders, and birches.

Cell—a (usually) microscopic unit of living matter bounded by a membrane or cell wall; or the wall itself after the contents have died.

Chlorophyll—the characteristic green pigment of plants, an essential pigment (or light absorber) in photosynthesis.

Compound—Composed of two or more similar parts, e.g., a compound leaf, divided into two or more leaflets with a common leafstalk.

Cone—a reproductive structure, either male or female, of certain trees consisting of a central axis surrounded by numerous woody or papery scales which bear the seeds or pollen, e.g., a pine cone.

Conifer—any cone-bearing tree such as pine, fir, or spruce; a major group of gymnosperms.

Crown—the leafy or branching head of a tree.

Deciduous—refers to a woody plant which sheds all its leaves annually, as opposed to being evergreen.

Dicotyledon—any member of a major subgroup of flowering plants (Dicotyledonae) characterized by embryos with two seed-leaves (cotyledons), net-veined leaves, and flower parts in fours or fives (as opposed to Monocotyledons).

Dioecious—producing male and female flowers or cones on separate individuals.

Epidermis—the outermost layer of cells in a given organ (e.g., a leaf.

Elliptical—having the shape of an ellipse, i.e., a "compressed circle."

Entire (margin)—smooth-edged; not toothed or cut.

Evergreen—refers to a woody plant having green leaves throughout the year, especially during the winter, as opposed to being deciduous.

Family—a category in the classification of plants and animals, ranking above a genus and below an order; including two or more related genera. Most plant family names end in -aceae.

Fern—any member of a broad division of nonflowering plants (Polypodiophyta) having true roots, stems, and specialized conduction tissue, and true leaves, which are usually large and compound or dissected. Reproduction is by spores, usually produced in sori on the lower surfaces or margins of the leaves.

Fern-ally—any member of several divisions of nonflowering plants which are akin to ferns, having true stems, leaves, and specialized conduction tissue and reproducing by spores, e.g., horsetails, quillworts, and clubmosses.

Flowering Plant—any member of a major group of vascular plants, known as angiosperms (Magnoliophyta), characterized by having true flowers, and seeds enclosed in a fruit.

Fathom—a unit of length equal to 1.8 metres (6 ft) used for measuring the depth of water.

Fertile—capable of producing viable seed, or as applied to stamens, capable of producing viable pollen.

-Foliate—a suffix indicating the number of leaflets in a compound leaf (e.g., 3-foliate—having three leaflets).

Follicle—a dry fruit composed of a single carpel which splits along the inner side at maturity.

Frond—the leaf of a fern, often compound or finely dissected.

Fruit—a ripened seed-case or ovary and any associated structures which ripen with it.

Fungi (fungus, singular)—a broad group of organisms, generally considered as plants, but lacking chlorophyll and true roots, stems, and leaves. Reproduction is by spores; includes moulds, mildews, rusts, smuts, and mushrooms.

Genus (genera, plural)—a category in the classification of plants and animals which is the main subdivision of a family. It consists of a group of closely related species. In the scientific name of an organism, the genus name is the first term and the initial letter is always capitalized (cf. *Acer macrophyllum,* broad-leafed maple).

Gymnosperm—any member of a major group of vascular plants (Pinophyta) characterized by having seeds or ovules which are not enclosed in a fruit, but instead are borne in cones or related structures. The conifers are an important subgroup of gymnosperms.

Herbaceous—not woody; having stems which die back to the ground at the end of the growing season.

Holdfast—a structure, usually with branching, root-like appendages, by which a seaweed is fastened to the surface it is growing on.

Indusium—a membranous structure covering the sori of many types of ferns.

Inflorescence—a flower head or cluster, or the arrangement of the flowers on the axis.

Leaflet—an ultimate unit of a compound leaf.

Lenticels—slightly raised areas, usually elongated, on the surface of the bark of certain trees and shrubs. The cells are more loosely arranged than in the surrounding tissue.

Linear—very long and narrow.

Lobed—having major divisions extending about halfway to the base or centre; often applied to leaves, such as oak or maple.

Monocotyledon—any member of a major subgroup of flowering plants (Monocotyledonae), having embryos with a single seed-leaf (cotyledon), parallel-veined leaves, and flower parts in threes (as opposed to Dicotyledons).

Monoecious—having separate male and female flowers, both types borne on the same individual plant.

Mycelium—the mass of minute tubular structures making up the main body of a fungus. It is typically embedded in a substrate such as wood or soil.

Node—a joint or portion of a stem from which a leaf or branch has grown.

Nut—a hard, dry, usually one-seeded fruit which remains closed at maturity.

Nutlet—diminutive of nut; a dry, closed half-arpel of the mint and borage families.

Opposite—growing directly across from each other at the same node (in reference to leaves).

Ovulate—pertaining to a female or seed-bearing reproductive structure such as a cone.

Ovule—a young or undeveloped seed.

Palmately compound—referring to a compound leaf with the leaflets arising from the same point, e.g., the leaf of a horse-chestnut or lupine.

Pedicel—a short stalk of a single flower in an inflorescence.

Perennial—a plant that lives more than two years.

Petal—any member of the inside set of floral bracts in flowering plants; usually coloured or white and serving to attract insect or bird pollinators. Many flowers do not have true petals.

Pinna (*pinnae,* plural)—one of the primary lateral divisions of a pinnately compound leaf such as a fern frond.

Pinnately compound—referring to a compound leaf with leaflets on either side of a central axis in a featherlike arrangement, e.g., the leaf of a walnut or elderberry.

Pinnule—an ultimate leaflet of a leaf which is pinnately compound two or more times, i.e., the ultimate division of a compound pinna.

Pistil—the female or seed-bearing organ of a flower, composed of one or more units or carpels, usually differentiated into ovary, style, and stigma.

Pistillate—refers to flowering structures having one or more pistils but no stamens.

Pollen—the mass of young male reproductive bodies (pollen grains) of a seed plant at the stage when they are released from the anther or pollen capsule.

Pores—minute crowded holes or tubules characteristic of pore fungi; these bear spore-producing structures on their surfaces.

Rhizome—a creeping underground stem, often fleshy, serving in vegetative reproduction and food storage.

Rootstock—an underground, root-like portion of a stem.

Rosette—a cluster of leaves (or other organs) arranged in a circle or disc, often at the base of a plant.

Scale—any small, thin or flat structure.

Sepal—any member of the outside set of floral bracts in flowering plants; typically green and leaf-like, but sometimes bright-coloured and petal-like.

Sheath—a thin covering surrounding an organ, such as the sheath of a grass leaf, which surrounds the stem.

Shrub—a relatively small woody perennial, usually with several permanent stems instead of a trunk like that of a tree.

Silicon—a non-metallic element which, combined with oxygen as silicon dioxide, is a major component of such substances as quartz, opal, and sand.

Simple leaf—a leaf with the blade all in one piece, i.e., not compound.

Soredia—powdery granules borne on the thallus of some lichens.

Sorus (*sori,* plural)—a cluster of spore cases on the undersurface of a fern frond.

Species (singular or plural)—the fundamental unit in the classification of plants and animals, comprising a subdivision of a genus, and consisting of a group of organisms having a high degree of similarity, which usually interbreed only amongst themselves and show persistent differences from members of related species. In a scientific name, the species is designated by the second term, which is never capitalized (cf. *Acer macrophyllum,* broad-leafed maple).

Spike—an elongated flower cluster, with flowers attached directly to the central stalk.

Spikelet—diminutive of spike; an ultimate flowering unit in a compound inflorescence, especially in grasses.

Sporangium (*sporangia,* plural)—a spore case or container.

Spore—a one-celled reproductive structure in non-flowering plants such as mosses and ferns, corresponding to a seed, but lacking an embryo.

Stamen—the male or pollen-bearing organ of a flower, consisting of a pollen capsule, or anther, and a stalk, or filament.

Staminate—refers to flowering structures having one or more stamens but no pistils.

Stipe—an erect stem-like portion of a seaweed.

Stomata—openings in the outer tissue of a leaf which allow the exchange of gases between the inner leaf cells and the atmosphere. Under certain conditions they can be closed off by "guard cells" around the openings.

Subtidal—below the lowest low-tide level.

Terminal—growing at the end of a stem or branch.

Thallus—a plant body (e.g., lichen) which is not clearly differentiated into roots, stems, and leaves.

Tree—a (large) woody perennial having a single elongate main stem or trunk.

Umbel—a flower head in which the stems of individual flowers or flower clusters spring from a common point on the stem, like spokes of an umbrella.

Vegetative—relating to plants or parts of plants lacking reproductive structures.

Whorl—a ring of three or more similar structures (e.g., leaves or branches) radiating from a node or common point.

REFERENCES

BANDONI, R. J., and A. F. SZCZAWINSKI.

    1976. *Guide to Common Mushrooms of British Columbia.* British Columbia Provincial Museum Handbook No. 24, Victoria.

BARNETT, H. G.

    1955. *The Coast Salish of British Columbia.* University of Oregon Press, Eugene.

BOAS, F.

    1921. *Ethnology of the Kwakiutl.* Bureau of American Ethnology, 35th Annual Report, Pt. 1, 1913–14. Smithsonian Institution, Washington.

BOUCHARD, R.

    1973. *Mainland Comox Plant Names.* Unpublished manuscript. British Columbia Indian Language Project, Victoria.

BRAYSHAW, T. C.

    1976. *Catkin Bearing Plants of British Columbia.* British Columbia Provincial Museum Occasional Paper No. 18, Victoria.

BRITISH COLUMBIA DEPARTMENT OF EDUCATION, DIVISION OF CURRICULUM.

    1951–63. *British Columbia Heritage Series: Our Native Peoples.* Victoria. 10 Volumes. 1. Introduction to Our Native Peoples; 2. Coast Salish; 3. Interior Salish; 4. Haida; 5. Nootka; 6. Tsimshian; 7. Kwakiutl; 8. Kootenay; 9. Déné; 10. Bella Coola.

CALDER, J. A., and R. L. TAYLOR.

    1968. *Flora of the Queen Charlotte Islands.* Part 1. Canada Department of Agriculture, Research Branch, Monograph No. 4, Ottawa.

CARLSON, R. L. (ed.).

    1970. *Archaeology in British Columbia, New Discoveries.* Special Issue of *B.C. Studies.* University of British Columbia, Vancouver. No. 6–7 (Fall-Winter).

CARRIER LINGUISTIC COMMITTEE.

    1973. *Hanúyeh Ghun 'Útni-i.* (*Plants of Carrier Country.*) Central Carrier Language. Fort St. James.

CHAMBERLAIN, A. B.

    1892. Report on the Kootenay Indians of Southeastern British Columbia. *Eighth Report on the Northwestern Tribes of Canada.* British Association for the Advancement of Science. Edinburgh Meeting.

CLARK, L. J.

    1973. *Wild Flowers of British Columbia.* Gray's Publishing Ltd., Sidney.

COVILLE, F. V.

    1904. Plants used in basketry. In: O. T. Mason. *Aborginal American Basketry.* Report of the U.S. National Museum. Government Printing Office, Washington.

DAVIDSON, J.

    1927. *Conifers, Junipers and Yew: Gymnosperms of British Columbia.* T. Fisher Unwin Ltd., London.

DEPARTMENT OF INDIAN AFFAIRS AND NORTHERN DEVELOPMENT.

    1970. *Linguistic and Cultural Affiliations of Canadian Indian Bands.* Indian Affairs Branch, Ottawa.

DRIVER, H. E.

    1961. *Indians of North America.* The University of Chicago Press, Chicago.

DRUCKER, P.

    1951. *The Northern and Central Nootkan Tribes.* Bureau of American Ethnology, Bulletin 44. Smithsonian Institution, Washington.

1955. *Indians of the Northwest Coast.* Natural History Press, Garden City.

1965. *Cultures of the North Pacific Coast.* Chandler Publishing Company, San Francisco.

DUFF, W.

1952. *The Upper Stalo Indians.* Anthropology in British Columbia, Memoir No. 1, British Columbia Provincial Museum, Victoria.

1964. *The Indian History of British Columbia, Vol. 1. The Impact of the White Man.* Anthropology in British Columbia, Memoir No. 5, British Columbia Provincial Museum, Victoria.

———— and M. KEW.

1973. A Select Bibliography of Anthropology In British Columbia. *B.C. Studies,* University of British Columbia, Vancouver. No. 19 (Autumn), pp. 73–122. (Revised by F. Woodward and Laine Ruus.)

EASTHAM, J. W.

1947. *Supplement to "Flora of Southern British Columbia" (J. K. Henry).* British Columbia Provincial Museum, Special Publication No. 1, Victoria.

ELLIS, D. W.

1976A. *The Knowledge and Usage of Marine Invertebrates by the Skidegate Haida People of the Queen Charlotte Islands.* Unpublished manuscript. The Queen Charlotte Islands Museum Society, Skidegate.

1976B. *The Knowledge and Usage of Marine Invertebrates, Insects, Reptiles, and Amphibians by the Manhousat People of the West Coast of Vancouver Island.* Unpublished manuscript. Skidegate.

EMMONS, G. T.

1903. The Basketry of the Tlingit. *Memoirs of the American Museum of Natural History,* New York, Vol. 3, Pt. 2.

1911. *The Tahltan Indians.* University of Pennsylvania (The Museum) Anthropological Publications, Vol. 4 (1), Philadelphia.

GARMAN, E. H.

    1963. *Pocket Guide to Trees and Shrubs in British Columbia.* British Columbia Provincial Museum Handbook No. 31, Victoria.

GUNTHER, E.

    1945 (revised in 1973). *Ethnobotany of Western Washington.* University of Washington Publications in Anthropology Vol. 10, No. 1. University of Washington Press, Seattle.

HAEBERLIN, H. K., J. A. TEIT, and H. H. ROBERTS.

    1928. Coiled Basketry in British Columbia and Surrounding Region. *Bureau of American Ethnology, 41st Annual Report,* pp. 119–484, Smithsonian Institution, Washington.

HART, J.

    1974. *Plant Taxonomy of the Salish and Kootenai Indians of Western Montana.* Unpublished M.A. Thesis, University of Montana, Missoula.

HELLSON, J. C., and M. GADD.

    1974. *Ethnobotany of the Blackfoot Indians.* National Museum of Man. Mercury Series. Canadian Ethnology Service Paper No. 19. National Museum of Man, National Museums of Canada. Ottawa.

HENRY, J. K.

    1915. *Flora of Southern British Columbia and Vancouver Island.* W. J. Gage & Co. Ltd., Toronto.

HITCHCOCK, C. L., A. CRONQUIST, M. OWNBEY, and J. W. THOMPSON.

    1955–69. *Vascular Plants of the Pacific Northwest,* Pts. 1–5. University of Washington Press, Seattle.

HUBBARD, W. A.

    1969. *The Grasses of British Columbia.* British Columbia Provincial Museum Handbook No. 9, Victoria.

HULTÉN, E.

    1968. *Flora of Alaska and Neighboring Territories.* Stanford University Press, Stanford.

KRAJINA, V. J.

    1969. Ecology of Forest Trees in British Columbia. *Ecology of Western North America,* Vol. 2, No. 1.

JENNESS, D.

    (n.d.) The Saanich Indians and Coast Salish Field Notes. Unpublished manuscripts. National Museum of Man, Ethnology Archives Ms. #1103.6. National Museums of Canada. (Ethnobotanical excerpts by David Rozen, Victoria.)

JOHNSTON, A.

    1970. Blackfoot Indian Utilization of the Flora of the Northwestern Great Plains. *Economic Botany,* Vol. 24., No. 3: 301–324.

KENNEDY, D. I. D. AND R. BOUCHARD.

    1974. *Utilization of Fishes, Beach Foods, and Marine Animals by the Tl'úhus Indian People of British Columbia.* Unpublished manuscript. British Columbia Indian Language Project, Victoria.

    1975A. *Utilization of Fish by the Chase Shuswap Indian People of British Columbia.* Unpublished manuscript. British Columbia Indian Language Project, Victoria.

    1975B. *Utilization of Fish by the Colville Okanagan Indian People.* Unpublished manuscript. British Columbia Indian Language Project, Victoria.

    1975C. *Utilization of Fish by the Mount Currie Lillooet Indian People of British Columbia.* Unpublished manuscript. British Columbia Indian Language Project, Victoria.

    1976. *Utilization of Fish, Beach Foods, and Marine Mammals by the Squamish Indian People of British Columbia.* Unpublished manuscript. British Columbia Indian Language Project, Victoria.

LEECHMAN, D.

  1932. Aboriginal Paints and Dyes in Canada. *Transactions of the Royal Society of Canada.* Section II, 1932, pp. 37–42.

LYONS, C. P.

  1952 (revised 1965). *Trees, Shrubs and Flowers to Know in British Columbia.* J. M. Dent & Sons (Canada) Limited, Vancouver.

MCILWRAITH, T. F.

  1948. *The Bella Coola Indians,* 2 Volumes. University of Toronto Press, Toronto.

MCNEARY, S.

  1974. *The Traditional Economic and Social Life of the Niska.* Unpublished Report, National Museum of Man, Ottawa.

  1976. *Where Fire Came Down. Social and Economic Life of the Niska.* Unpublished Ph.D. Thesis. Bryn Mawr College, Bryn Mawr, Pa.

MORICE, REV. FATHER A. G. (O.M.I.)

  1893. Notes Archaeological, Industrial, and Sociological on the Western Dénés. *Transactions of the Canadian Institute,* Session 1892–93.

NEWCOMBE, C. F.

  1902–1910. Unpublished field notes on Nootka, Haida, and Salishan groups. British Columbia Provincial Archives, Victoria.

PALMER, G.

  1975. Shuswap Indian Ethnobotany. *Syesis,* Vol. 8, pp. 29–81.

SCAGEL, R. F.

  1967. *Guide to Common Seaweeds of British Columbia.* British Columbia Provincial Museum Handbook No. 27, Victoria.

SCHOFIELD, W. B.

    1969. *Some Common Mosses of British Columbia.* British Columbia Provincial Museum Handbook No. 28, Victoria.

SMITH, H. I.

    1927. *Handbook of the Kitwanga Garden of Native Plants.* National Museum of Canada and Department of Indian Affairs, Ottawa.

SPROAT, G. M.

    1868. *Scenes and Studies of Savage Life.* London.

STEEDMAN, E. V.

    1929. The Ethnobotany of the Thompson Indians of British Columbia. *Bureau of American Ethnology, 45th Annual Report,* 1927–28. Smithsonian Institution, Washington.

SWANTON, J.

    1905. *Contributions to the Ethnology of the Haida.* American Museum of Natural History, Memoir No. 8, Part 1; Jesup North Pacific Expedition, Vol. 5, Pt. 1.

SZCZAWINSKI, A. F.

    1962. *The Heather Family (Ericaceae) of British Columbia.* British Columbia Provincial Museum Handbook No. 19, Victoria.

TAYLOR, T. M. C.

    1956. *The Ferns and Fern-allies of British Columbia.* British Columbia Provincial Museum Handbook No. 12, Victoria.

    1966. *The Lily Family (Liliaceae) of British Columbia.* British Columbia Provincial Museum Handbook No. 25, Victoria.

    1973. *The Rose Family (Rosaceae) of British Columbia.* British Columbia Provincial Museum Handbook No. 30, Victoria.

11

1974A. *The Pea Family (Leguminosae) of British Columbia.* British Columbia Provincial Museum Handbook No. 32, Victoria.

1974B. *The Figwort Family (Scrophulariaceae) of British Columbia.* British Columbia Provincial Museum Handbook No. 33, Victoria.

TEIT, J. A.

1900. *The Thompson Indians.* American Museum of Natural History, Memoir No. 2.

1906A. *The Lillooet Indians.* American Museum of Natural History, Memoir No. 4.

1906B. Notes on the Tahltan Indians of British Columbia. *Boas Anniversary Volume.* New York, pp. 337–349.

1909. *The Shuswap.* American Musuem of Natural History, Memoir No. 5.

1930. The Salishan Tribes of the Western Plateaus. *Bureau of American Ethnology, 45th Annual Report, 1927–28.* Smithsonian Institution, Washington.

TURNER, N. J.

1973. The Ethnobotany of the Bella Coola Indians of British Columbia. *Syesis,* Vol. 6, pp. 193–220.

1975. *Food Plants of British Columbia Indians.* Part 1. *Coastal Peoples.* British Columbia Provincial Museum Handbook No. 34, Victoria.

1978. *Food Plants of British Columbia Indians.* Part 2. *Interior Peoples.* British Columbia Provincial Museum Handbook No. 36, Victoria.

——— and M. A. M. BELL.

1971. The Ethnobotany of the Coast Salish Indians of Vancouver Island. *Economic Botany,* Vol. 25, No. 1: pp. 63–104.

1973. The Ethnobotany of the Southern Kwakiutl Indians of British Columbia. *Economic Botany,* Vol. 27, No. 3: pp. 257–310.

—————, R. BOUCHARD, and D. I. D. KENNEDY.
   1975.   *The Ethnobotany of the Okanagan-speaking Indians
          of British Columbia and Washington State.*   Unpublished
          manuscript, Victoria.
————— and D. W. ELLIS.
   1976.   *Nootka Plant Notes, from Manhousat (Hotspring
          Cove),* made with Luke Swan.   Unpublished manuscript,
          Victoria.

INDEX

(Pages in bold face indicate where detailed discussion of plant occurs.)

304

BRITISH COLUMBIA PROVINCIAL MUSEUM PUBLICATIONS

(Prices subject to change without notice)
(Sales tax not applicable)

Publications may go out of print from time to time; therefore, purchasers should inquire about the status of a particular publication before placing their order.

Please address orders and inquiries to

PUBLICATIONS,
British Columbia Provincial Museum,
Victoria, B.C.
V8V 1X4
Phone (604) 387-3701

Make cheques or money orders, in Canadian funds, payable to the Minister of Finance, Province of British Columbia.

Printed by K. M. MACDONALD, Printer to the Queen's Most Excellent Majesty
in right of the Province of British Columbia.
1979

Q